FE civil practice exam

978-1-932613-97-1

Copyright ©2020 by NCEES®. All rights reserved.

All NCEES sample questions and solutions are copyrighted under the laws of the United States. No part of this publication may be reproduced, stored in a retrieval system, or transmitted in any form or by any means without the prior written permission of NCEES. Requests for permissions should be addressed in writing to permissions@ncees.org.

ISBN 978-1-932613-97-1

Printed in the United States of America
1st printing January 2020

CONTENTS

About NCEES

NCEES is a nonprofit organization made up of the U.S. engineering and surveying licensing boards in all 50 states, U.S. territories, and the District of Columbia. We develop and score the exams used for engineering and surveying licensure in the United States. NCEES also promotes professional mobility through its services for licensees and its member boards.

Engineering licensure in the United States is regulated by licensing boards in each state and territory. These boards set and maintain the standards that protect the public they serve. As a result, licensing requirements and procedures vary by jurisdiction, so stay in touch with your board (ncees.org/licensing-boards).

Exam Format

The FE exam contains 110 questions and is administered year-round via computer at approved Pearson VUE test centers. A 6-hour appointment time includes a tutorial, the exam, and a break. You'll have 5 hours and 20 minutes to complete the actual exam.

In addition to traditional multiple-choice questions with one correct answer, the FE exam uses common alternative item types such as

- Multiple correct options—allows multiple choices to be correct
- Point and click—requires examinees to click on part of a graphic to answer
- Drag and drop—requires examinees to click on and drag items to match, sort, rank, or label
- Fill in the blank—provides a space for examinees to enter a response to the question

To familiarize yourself with the format, style, and navigation of a computer-based exam, view the demo on ncees.org/ExamPrep.

Examinee Guide

The *NCEES Examinee Guide* is the official guide to policies and procedures for all NCEES exams. During exam registration and again on exam day, examinees must agree to abide by the conditions in the *Examinee Guide*, which includes the CBT Examinee Rules and Agreement. You can download the *Examinee Guide* at ncees.org/exams. It is your responsibility to make sure you have the current version.

Scoring and reporting

Exam results for computer-based exams are typically available 7–10 days after you take the exam. You will receive an email notification from NCEES with instructions to view your results in your MyNCEES account. All results are reported as pass or fail.

Updates on exam content and procedures

Visit us at **ncees.org/exams** for updates on everything exam-related, including specifications, exam-day policies, scoring, and corrections to published exam preparation materials. This is also where you will register for the exam and find additional steps you should follow in your state to be approved for the exam.

EXAM SPECIFICATIONS

Fundamentals of Engineering (FE)
CIVIL CBT Exam Specifications

Effective Beginning with the July 2020 Examinations

- The FE exam is a computer-based test (CBT). It is closed book with an electronic reference.
- Examinees have 6 hours to complete the exam, which contains 110 questions. The 6-hour time also includes a tutorial and an optional scheduled break.
- The FE exam uses both the International System of Units (SI) and the U.S. Customary System (USCS).

Knowledge	Number of Questions
1. Mathematics and Statistics A. Analytic geometry B. Single-variable calculus C. Vector operations D. Statistics (e.g., distributions, mean, mode, standard deviation, confidence interval, regression and curve fitting)	**8–12**
2. Ethics and Professional Practice A. Codes of ethics (professional and technical societies) B. Professional liability C. Licensure D. Contracts and contract law	**4–6**
3. Engineering Economics A. Time value of money (e.g., equivalence, present worth, equivalent annual worth, future worth, rate of return) B. Cost (e.g., fixed, variable, direct and indirect labor, incremental, average, sunk) C. Analyses (e.g., break-even, benefit-cost, life cycle, sustainability, renewable energy) D. Uncertainty (e.g., expected value and risk)	**5–8**
4. Statics A. Resultants of force systems B. Equivalent force systems C. Equilibrium of rigid bodies D. Frames and trusses E. Centroid of area F. Area moments of inertia G. Static friction	**8–12**

5. Dynamics **4–6**

A. Kinematics (e.g., particles, rigid bodies)
B. Mass moments of inertia
C. Force acceleration (e.g., particles, rigid bodies)
D. Work, energy, and power (e.g., particles, rigid bodies)

6. Mechanics of Materials **7–11**

A. Shear and moment diagrams
B. Stresses and strains (e.g., diagrams, axial, torsion, bending, shear, thermal)
C. Deformations (e.g., axial, torsion, bending, thermal)
D. Combined stresses, principal stresses, and Mohr's circle
E. Elastic and plastic deformations

7. Materials **5–8**

A. Mix design of concrete and asphalt
B. Test methods and specifications of metals, concrete, aggregates, asphalt, and wood
C. Physical and mechanical properties of metals, concrete, aggregates, asphalt, and wood

8. Fluid Mechanics **6–9**

A. Flow measurement
B. Fluid properties
C. Fluid statics
D. Energy, impulse, and momentum of fluids

9. Surveying **6–9**

A. Angles, distances, and trigonometry
B. Area computations
C. Earthwork and volume computations
D. Coordinate systems (e.g., state plane, latitude/longitude)
E. Leveling (e.g., differential, elevations, percent grades)

10. Water Resources and Environmental Engineering **10–15**

A. Basic hydrology (e.g., infiltration, rainfall, runoff, watersheds)
B. Basic hydraulics (e.g., Manning equation, Bernoulli theorem, open-channel flow)
C. Pumps
D. Water distribution systems
E. Flood control (e.g., dams, routing, spillways)
F. Stormwater (e.g., detention, routing, quality)
G. Collection systems (e.g., wastewater, stormwater)
H. Groundwater (e.g., flow, wells, drawdown)
I. Water quality (e.g., ground and surface, basic water chemistry)
J. Testing and standards (e.g., water, wastewater, air, noise)
K. Water and wastewater treatment (e.g., biological processes, softening, drinking water treatment)

11. **Structural Engineering** **10–15**

A. Analysis of statically determinant beams, columns, trusses, and frames
B. Deflection of statically determinant beams, trusses, and frames
C. Column analysis (e.g., buckling, boundary conditions)
D. Structural determinacy and stability analysis of beams, trusses, and frames
E. Elementary statically indeterminate structures
F. Loads, load combinations, and load paths (e.g., dead, live, lateral, influence lines and moving loads, tributary areas)
G. Design of steel components (e.g., codes and design philosophies, beams, columns, tension members, connections)
H. Design of reinforced concrete components (e.g., codes and design philosophies, beams, columns)

12. **Geotechnical Engineering** **10–15**

A. Index properties and soil classifications
B. Phase relations
C. Laboratory and field tests
D. Effective stress
E. Stability of retaining structures (e.g., active/passive/at-rest pressure)
F. Shear strength
G. Bearing capacity
H. Foundation types (e.g., spread footings, deep foundations, wall footings, mats)
I. Consolidation and differential settlement
J. Slope stability (e.g., fills, embankments, cuts, dams)
K. Soil stabilization (e.g., chemical additives, geosynthetics)

13. **Transportation Engineering** **9–14**

A. Geometric design (e.g., streets, highways, intersections)
B. Pavement system design (e.g., thickness, subgrade, drainage, rehabilitation)
C. Traffic capacity and flow theory
D. Traffic control devices
E. Transportation planning (e.g., travel forecast modeling, safety, trip generation)

14. **Construction Engineering** **8–12**

A. Project administration (e.g., documents, management, procurement, project delivery methods)
B. Construction operations and methods (e.g., safety, equipment, productivity analysis, temporary erosion control)
C. Project controls (e.g., earned value, scheduling, allocation of resources, activity relationships)
D. Construction estimating
E. Interpretation of engineering drawings

PRACTICE EXAM

1. The area of the shaded portion of the figure shown below is most nearly:

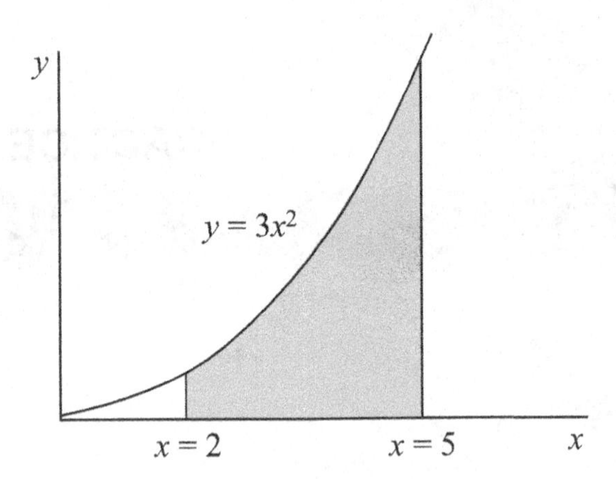

- ○ A. 18
- ○ B. 39
- ○ C. 117
- ○ D. 133

2. The indefinite integral of $x^3 - x + 1$ is:

- ○ A. $3x^2 - 1 + C$
- ○ B. $\frac{x^4}{3} - \frac{x^2}{2} + 1 + C$
- ○ C. $\frac{x^4}{3} - \frac{x^2}{2} + 1$
- ○ D. $\frac{x^4}{4} - \frac{x^2}{2} + x + C$

Copyright © 2020 by NCEES

3. The integral $\int_2^4 \frac{1}{x^2}\,dx$ equals

- ○ A. $\frac{1}{4}$
- ○ B. $\frac{3}{4}$
- ○ C. $-\frac{3}{16}$
- ○ D. $\frac{5}{16}$

4. If $y = 4x^3 + 3x^2z + 5xz^2 + 6z^3 + 20$, then $\left(\frac{\partial^2 y}{\partial x^2}\right) =$

- ○ A. $12x + 6z$
- ○ B. $24x + 6z$
- ○ C. $12x^2 + 6xz + 5z^2$
- ○ D. $24x^2 + 6xz + 5z^2$

Copyright © 2020 by NCEES

5. The following data have been collected:

Test	Average Score
1	85
2	87
3	95
4	90
5	85
6	88
7	90
8	90
9	91

Which of the following statements is true?

- ○ A. The median and the mode are equal.
- ○ B. The mean and the median are equal.
- ○ C. The mean and the mode are equal.
- ○ D. The mean is larger than both the mode and the median.

6. Which of the following is a unit vector perpendicular to the plane determined by the vectors $\mathbf{A} = 2\mathbf{i} + 4\mathbf{j}$ and $\mathbf{B} = \mathbf{i} + \mathbf{j} - \mathbf{k}$?

- ○ A. $-2\mathbf{i} + \mathbf{j} - \mathbf{k}$
- ○ B. $\frac{1}{\sqrt{5}}(\mathbf{i} + 2\mathbf{j})$
- ○ C. $\frac{1}{\sqrt{6}}(-2\mathbf{i} + \mathbf{j} - \mathbf{k})$
- ○ D. $\frac{1}{\sqrt{6}}(-2\mathbf{i} - \mathbf{j} - \mathbf{k})$

Copyright © 2020 by NCEES

7. You throw two 6-sided fair dice. The probability that the sum will be less than 12 is most nearly:

- ○ A. 0.028
- ○ B. 0.083
- ○ C. 0.333
- ○ D. 0.972

8. The water content of a soil volume is measured four times gravimetrically by oven drying. The mean value of the water content is 23.2%. If the standard deviation of the four measurements is 1.0%, the 99% confidence interval for the soil water content is most nearly:

- ○ A. (18.6%, 27.8%)
- ○ B. (19.5%, 26.9%)
- ○ C. (20.6%, 25.8%)
- ○ D. (20.9%, 25.5%)

9. According to the *Model Rules*, Section 240.15, Rules of Professional Conduct, licensed professional engineers are obligated to:

- ○ A. ensure that design documents and surveys are reviewed by a panel of licensed engineers prior to affixing a seal of approval
- ○ B. express public opinions under the direction of an employer or client regardless of knowledge of subject matter
- ○ C. practice by performing services only in the areas of their competence and in accordance with the current standards of technical competence
- ○ D. offer, give, or solicit services directly or indirectly in order to secure work or other valuable or political considerations

Copyright © 2020 by NCEES

10. An engineer testifying as an expert witness in a product liability case should:

- ○ A. answer as briefly as possible only those questions posed by the attorneys
- ○ B. provide an evaluation of the character of the defendant
- ○ C. provide a complete and objective analysis within his or her area of competence
- ○ D. provide information on the professional background of the defendant

11. As a professional engineer originally licensed 30 years ago, you are asked to evaluate a newly developed computerized control system for a public transportation system. The owner requires a currently licensed engineer to evaluate the system. You may accept this project if:

Select **all** that apply.

- ☐ A. you are competent in the area of computerized control systems
- ☐ B. your professional engineering license has lapsed, but you have two FE interns working for you
- ☐ C. you took a transportation course in college
- ☐ D. you have regularly attended meetings of a professional engineering society
- ☐ E. you have another licensed engineer work for you who is competent in this area, and he or she will conduct all related work and stamp the related design

12. A lien is a:

- ○ A. claim on property for payment of a debt
- ○ B. requirement that a contractor secure a performance bond for a project
- ○ C. requirement that a contractor secure a payment bond for a project
- ○ D. claim for damages for lack of specific performance

Copyright © 2020 by NCEES

13. A company borrows $100,000 today at 12% nominal annual interest. The monthly payment of a 5-yr loan is most nearly:

- ○ A. $1,667
- ○ B. $2,200
- ○ C. $3,100
- ○ D. $12,000

14. You must choose between four pieces of comparable equipment based on the costs and salvage values given below. All four pieces have a life of 8 years.

Parameter	Equipment			
	A	B	C	D
First cost	$25,000	$35,000	$20,000	$40,000
Annual costs	$8,000	$6,000	$9,000	$5,000
Salvage value	$2,500	$3,500	$2,000	$4,000

The discount rate is 12%. Ignore taxes. The two most preferable equipment pieces and the approximate difference between their present worth values based on least cost are:

- ○ A. A and C, $170
- ○ B. B and D, $170
- ○ C. A and C, $234
- ○ D. B and D, $234

15. A company can manufacture a product using hand tools. Tools will cost $1,000, and the manufacturing cost per unit will be $1.50. As an alternative, an automated system will cost $15,000 with a manufacturing cost per unit of $0.50. With an anticipated annual volume of 5,000 units and neglecting interest, the payback period (years) to invest in the automated system is most nearly:

- ○ A. 2.0
- ○ B. 2.8
- ○ C. 3.6
- ○ D. 15.0

Copyright © 2020 by NCEES

16. A construction company bought a new rubber-tire loader and is performing a risk analysis about whether to purchase insurance. The construction company paid $100,000 for the loader. The annual cost for the insurance premium is $2,000, and the deductible is $1,000. The risk options to purchase or not to purchase insurance are as follows:

- 0.88 probability of no accident
- 0.11 probability of a small accident at a cost of $800
- 0.01 probability of a total loss for the loader

The best option and projected cost savings are:

- A. purchase insurance and save $990
- B. purchase insurance and save $1,088
- C. do not purchase insurance and save $1,010
- D. do not purchase insurance and save $2,098

17. A tractor cost $7,500. After 10 years it has a salvage value of $5,000. Maintenance costs are $500 per year. If the interest rate is 10%, the equivalent uniform annual cost is most nearly:

- A. $500
- B. $750
- C. $1,400
- D. $2,000

Copyright © 2020 by NCEES

18. The magnitude (N) of the resultant of the three coplanar forces, A, B, and C, is most nearly:

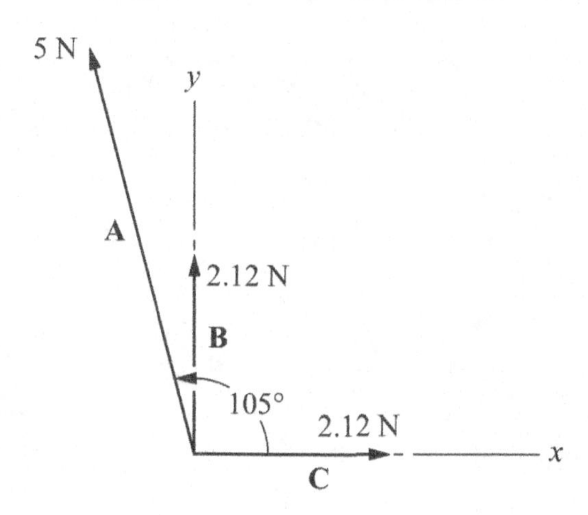

- ○ A. 7.0
- ○ B. 7.8
- ○ C. 9.2
- ○ D. 10.3

Copyright © 2020 by NCEES

19. A heavy roller is held in equilibrium on a frictionless Plane AB by the force **F**, as shown. Which diagram correctly shows a vector polygon of the forces acting on the roller?

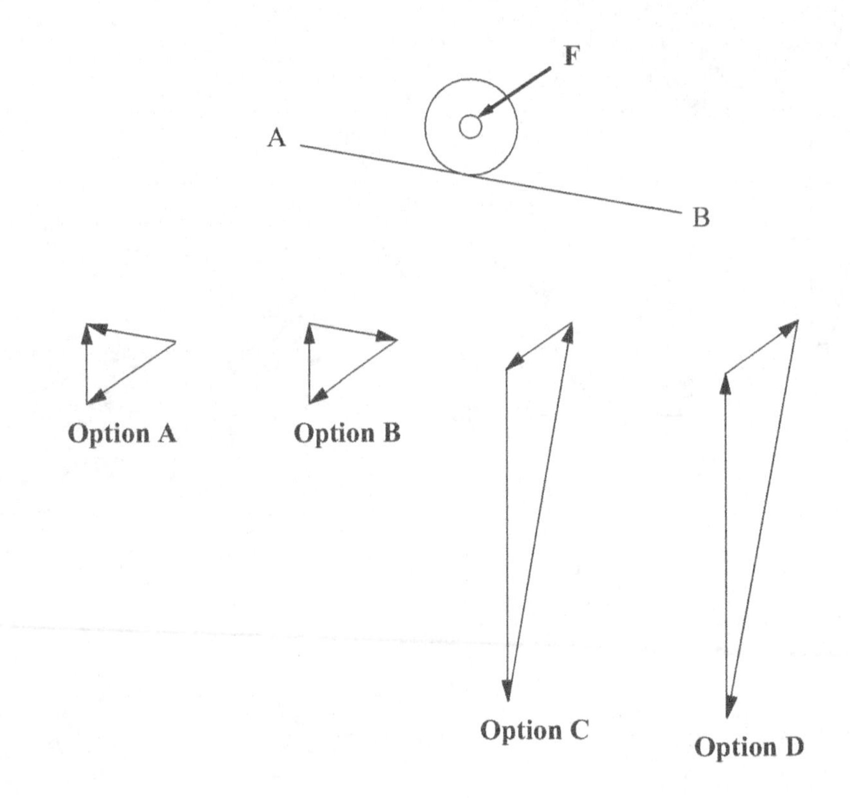

- ○ A. Option A
- ○ B. Option B
- ○ C. Option C
- ○ D. Option D

Copyright © 2020 by NCEES

20. Select the location on the x-axis where an additional load must be placed in order to achieve equilibrium of the L-shaped bar.

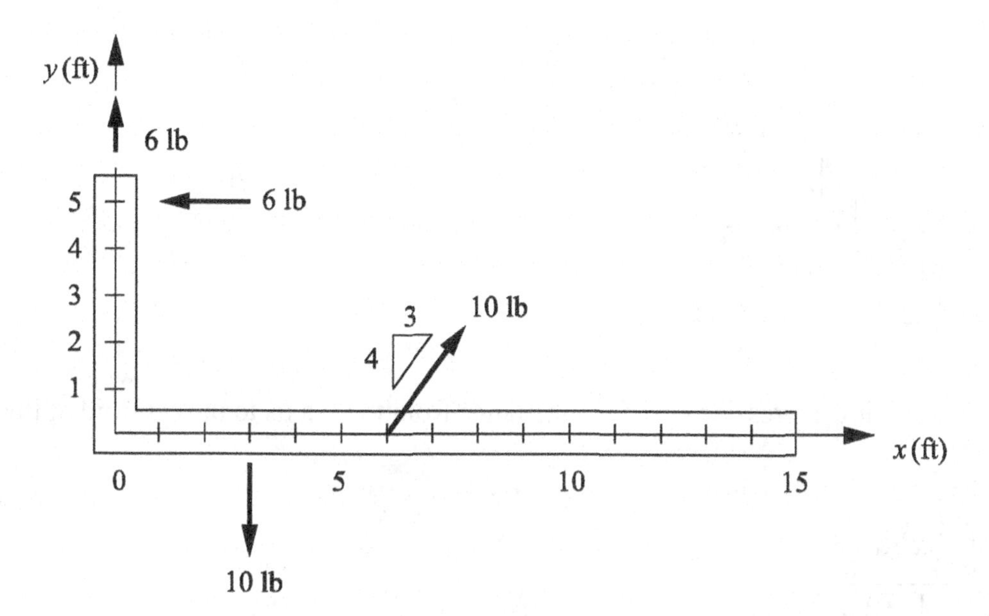

21. The figure below shows a simple truss. Which members in the truss have no (zero) force in them?

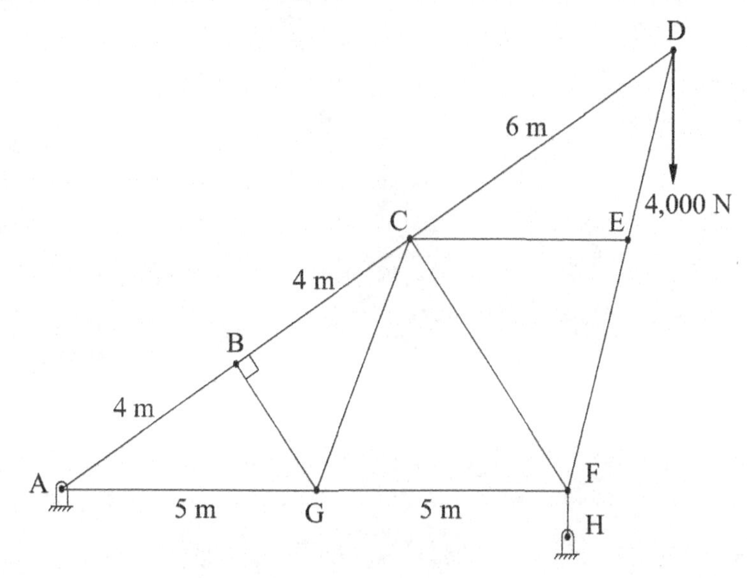

- ○ A. BG, CG, CF, CE
- ○ B. BG, CE
- ○ C. CG, CF
- ○ D. CF

Copyright © 2020 by NCEES

22. Consider the following graph:

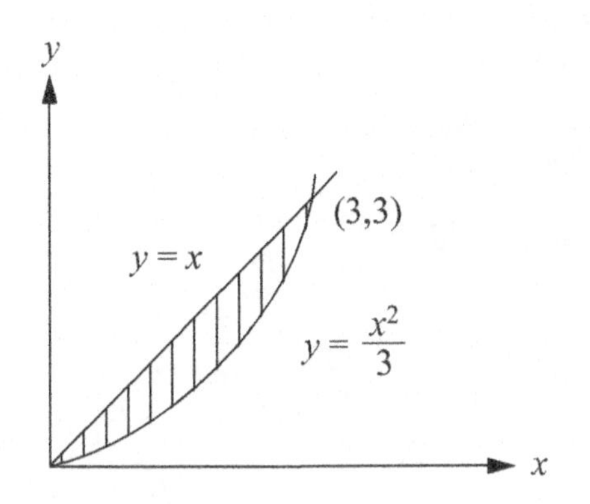

Which of the following expressions gives the distance from the y-axis to the centroid of the shaded area?

○ A. $$\frac{\int_0^3 \frac{1}{3}x^3 dx}{\int_0^3 \left(x + \frac{1}{3}x^2\right) dx}$$

○ B. $$\frac{\int_0^3 \left(x^2 - \frac{1}{3}x^3\right) dx}{\int_0^3 \left(x - \frac{1}{3}x^2\right) dx}$$

○ C. $$\frac{\int_0^3 \left(x - \frac{1}{3}x^2\right) dx}{\int_0^3 \left(x - \frac{1}{3}x^2\right) dx}$$

○ D. $$\frac{\int_0^3 \left(\frac{1}{2}x^2 + \frac{1}{3}x^3\right) dx}{\int_0^3 \left(x - \frac{1}{3}x^2\right) dx}$$

Copyright © 2020 by NCEES

23. The moment of inertia (in^4) of the area about the x' axis ($I_{x'}$) is most nearly:

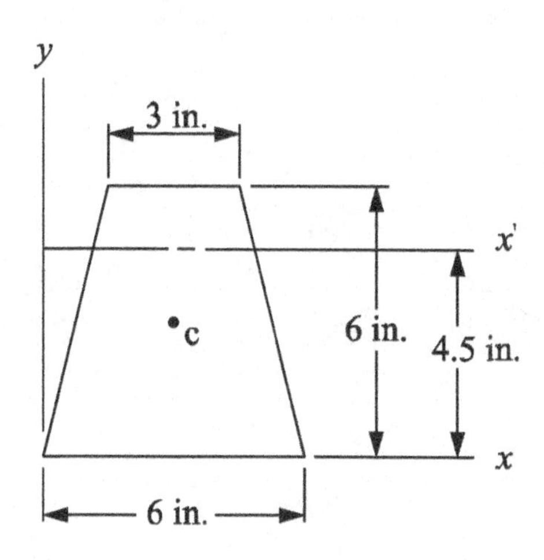

- A. 78.0
- B. 78.6
- C. 118.5
- D. 138.8

24. In the figure below, the coefficient of static friction between the block and the inclined plane is 0.25. The block is in equilibrium. As the inclined plane is raised, the block will begin to slide when:

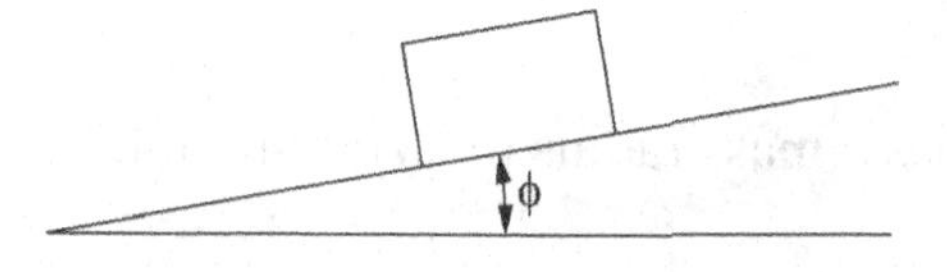

- A. $\sin \phi = 1.0$
- B. $\cos \phi = 1.0$
- C. $\cos \phi = 0.25$
- D. $\tan \phi = 0.25$

Copyright © 2020 by NCEES

25. Three forces act as shown below. The magnitude of the resultant of the three forces (N) is most nearly:

- O A. 140
- O B. 191
- O C. 370
- O D. 396

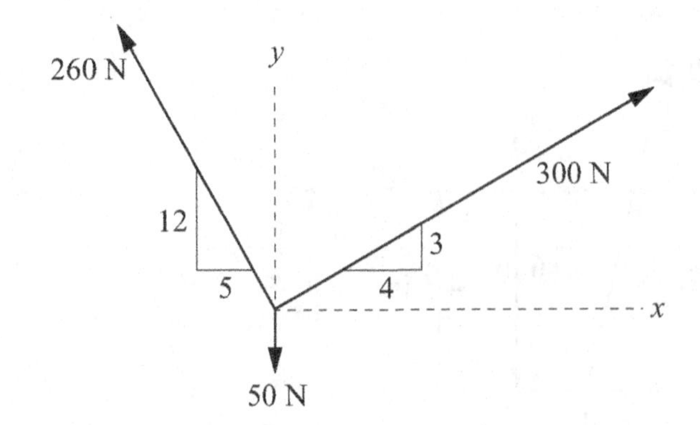

26. A boat accelerates at a constant rate of 12 ft/sec^2. The boat travels 140 ft while its speed changes to 60 ft/sec. The initial velocity (ft/sec) was most nearly:

- O A. 3.7
- O B. 5.0
- O C. 15.5
- O D. 31.0

27. A small rotating robotic arm weighs 8 N and has a mass radius of gyration of 4.0 cm. The mass moment of inertia (kg·cm^2) is most nearly:

- O A. 13.0
- O B. 32.0
- O C. 128
- O D. 256

Copyright © 2020 by NCEES

28. A 5-kg block is sliding along a frictionless surface and is an acted on by a constant force **P** of 20 N. The time (seconds) when the block is moving at 18 m/s is most nearly:

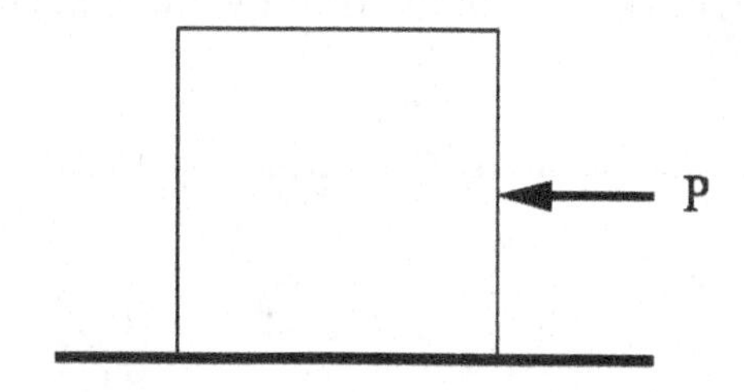

- ○ A. 0.22
- ○ B. 1.83
- ○ C. 4.50
- ○ D. 72.0

29. During impact of two objects, which of the following is true?

- ○ A. Energy is never conserved.
- ○ B. Energy is always conserved.
- ○ C. Momentum is never conserved.
- ○ D. Momentum is always conserved.

Copyright © 2020 by NCEES

30. The shear diagram for a particular beam is shown below. All lines in the diagram are straight. The bending moment at each end of the beam is zero, and there are no concentrated couples along the beam. The maximum magnitude of the bending moment (kN·m) in the beam is most nearly:

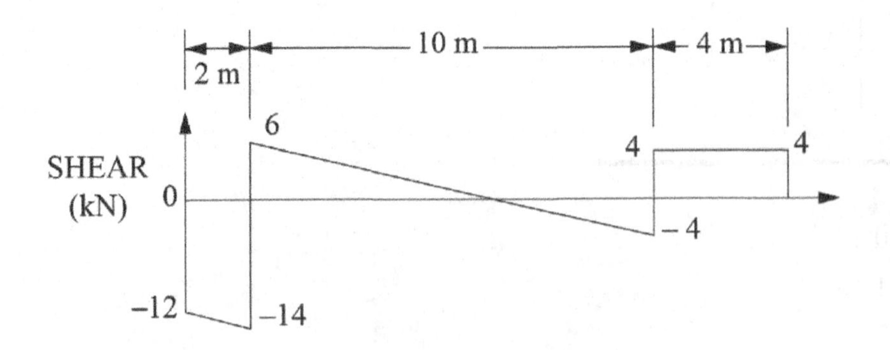

- ○ A. 8
- ○ B. 16
- ○ C. 18
- ○ D. 26

31. The pressure gauge in an air cylinder reads 1,680 kPa. The cylinder is constructed of a 12-mm rolled-steel plate with an internal diameter of 700 mm. The tangential stress (MPa) inside the tank is most nearly:

- ○ A. 25
- ○ B. 50
- ○ C. 77
- ○ D. 100

32. A 1-ft rod with a diameter of 0.5 in. is subjected to a tensile force of 1,300 lb and has an elongation of 0.009 in. The modulus of elasticity (ksi) of the material is most nearly:

- ○ A. 740
- ○ B. 884
- ○ C. 8,840
- ○ D. 10,000

Copyright © 2020 by NCEES

33. The maximum inplane shear stress (ksi) in the element shown below is most nearly:

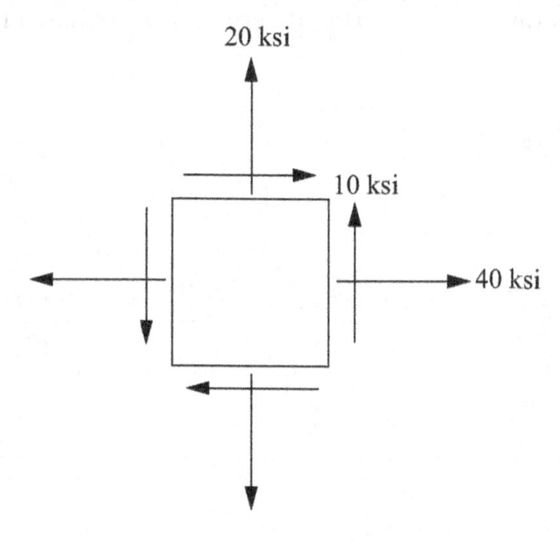

- ○ A. 10
- ○ B. 14.1
- ○ C. 44.1
- ○ D. 316

34. Based on the given stress-strain curves, which material has the largest plastic deformation?

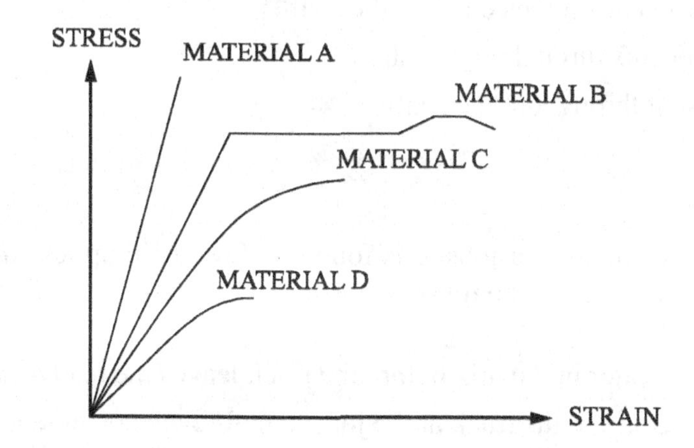

- ○ A. Material A
- ○ B. Material B
- ○ C. Material C
- ○ D. Material D

Copyright © 2020 by NCEES

35. The piston of a steam engine is 50 cm in diameter, and the maximum steam gauge pressure is 1.4 MPa. If the design stress for the piston rod is 68 MPa, its cross-sectional area (m^2) should be most nearly:

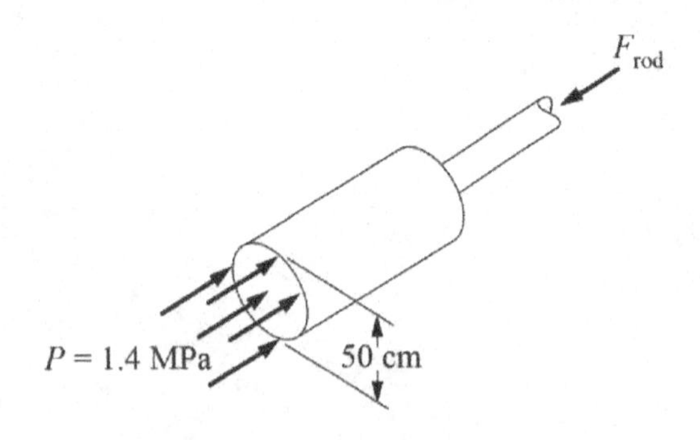

- O A. 40.4×10^{-4}
- O B. 98.8×10^{-4}
- O C. 228.0×10^{-4}
- O D. 323.0×10^{-4}

36. Which of the following is true when a circular shaft is subjected to torsion only?

- O A. Maximum shear stress occurs at the outermost fibers.
- O B. Maximum shear stress occurs at the center of the shaft.
- O C. Constant shear stress occurs throughout the shaft.
- O D. No shear stress is present throughout the shaft.

37. Ready-mixed concrete being delivered to a jobsite is found to have a slump less than specified. Without compromising strength, which of the following is the most appropriate corrective action?

- O A. Decrease the amount of water in the mix before the truck leaves the ready-mix plant.
- O B. Increase the water to the mix in the truck at the jobsite before the concrete is poured.
- O C. Add a water-reducing admixture to the mix in the truck at the jobsite before the concrete is poured.
- O D. Increase the rotation speed of the mixing drum while the truck is in transit to the jobsite.

Copyright © 2020 by NCEES

38. The test that measures the energy required to fracture a specimen at a given temperature is the:

- ○ A. Brinell Test
- ○ B. Rockwell Test
- ○ C. Endurance Test
- ○ D. Charpy Test

39. In general, a metal with high hardness will also have:

- ○ A. good formability
- ○ B. high impact strength
- ○ C. high electrical conductivity
- ○ D. high yield strength

40. The following preliminary concrete mix has been designed assuming that the aggregates are in oven-dry condition. However, the aggregates used are in SSD condition.

Water = 305 lb/yd^3
Cement = 693 lb/yd^3
Coarse aggregate (SSD) = 1,674 lb/yd^3
Fine aggregate (SSD) = 1,100 lb/yd^3

The properties of the aggregates are:

Property	Coarse Aggregate	Fine Aggregate
Moisture content at SSD	0.5%	0.7%
Moisture content as used in mix	2.0%	6.0%

The amount of water (lb/yd^3) that would be used in the final mix is most nearly:

- ○ A. 206
- ○ B. 222
- ○ C. 305
- ○ D. 388

Copyright © 2020 by NCEES

41. The solid line represents results from a uniaxial tension test. The slope of the dashed line is associated with which physical property of the material?

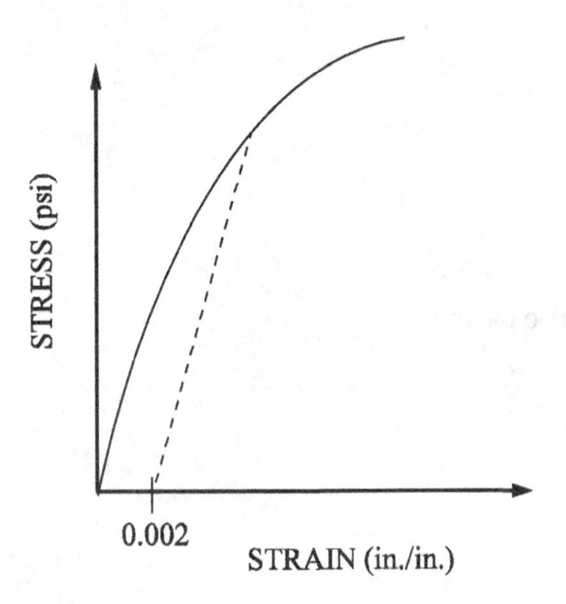

- ○ A. Yield strength
- ○ B. Yield strain
- ○ C. Secant modulus
- ○ D. Modulus of elasticity

42. The pitot tube shown below is placed at a point where the velocity is 2.0 m/s. The specific gravity of the fluid is 2.0, and the upper portion of the manometer contains air. The reading h (m) on the manometer is most nearly:

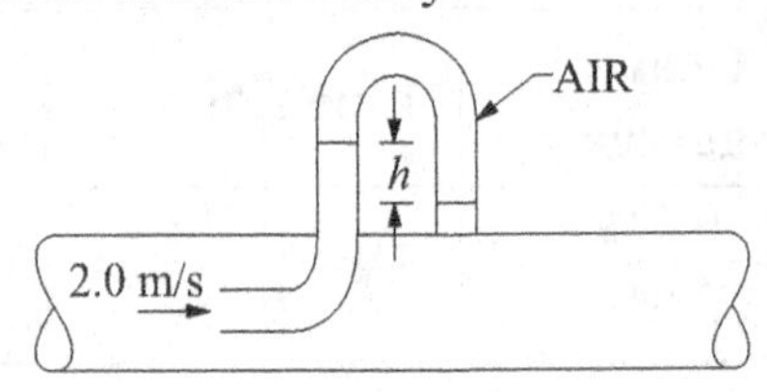

- ○ A. 20.0
- ○ B. 10.0
- ○ C. 0.40
- ○ D. 0.20

Copyright © 2020 by NCEES

43. If the standard density of water is 1,000 kg/m^3, a fluid having a specific gravity of 1.263 and an absolute dynamic viscosity of 1.5 kg/(m·s) has a kinematic viscosity (m^2/s) of most nearly:

○ A. 1.19×10^{-3}
○ B. 1.50×10^{-3}
○ C. 1.89×10^{-3}
○ D. 528

44. Archimedes' principle states that:

○ A. the sum of the pressure, velocity, and elevation heads is constant
○ B. flow passing two points in a stream is equal at each point
○ C. the buoyant force on a body is equal to the volume displaced by the body
○ D. a floating body displaces a weight of fluid equal to its own weight

Copyright © 2020 by NCEES

45. A 1-in-diameter jet of 50°F water is deflected 90° by an angled chute as shown. The water enters with a velocity of 25 ft/sec and freely exits into the atmosphere with the same velocity. The forces (lb) in the x and y directions of the chute are most nearly:

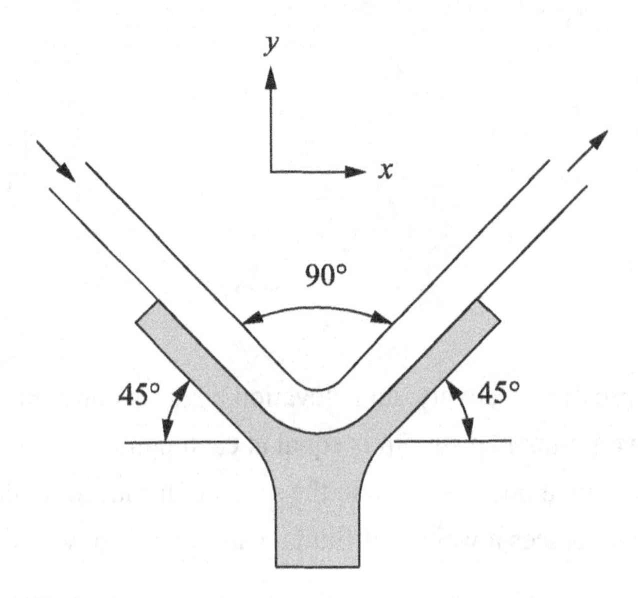

○ A. $F_x = 0$
$F_y = 0$

○ B. $F_x = 9.33$ lb
$F_y = 0$

○ C. $F_x = 0$
$F_y = 9.33$ lb

○ D. $F_x = 9.33$ lb
$F_y = 9.33$ lb

Copyright © 2020 by NCEES

46. The rectangular homogeneous gate shown below is 3.00 m high × 1.00 m wide and has a frictionless hinge at the bottom. If the fluid on the left side of the gate has a density of 1,600 kg/m^3, the magnitude of the force **F** (kN) required to keep the gate closed is most nearly:

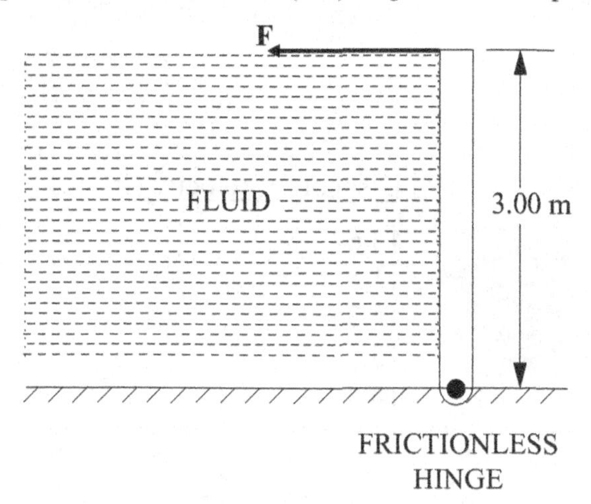

- A. 0
- B. 22
- C. 24
- D. 220

47. Four water tanks are shown with varying water heights H and varying nozzle cross-sectional areas A_0. Assume no minor losses in the discharge and a common coefficient of discharge $C = 0.6$ for all the nozzles. Match the discharge velocity (ft/sec) to the correct tank.

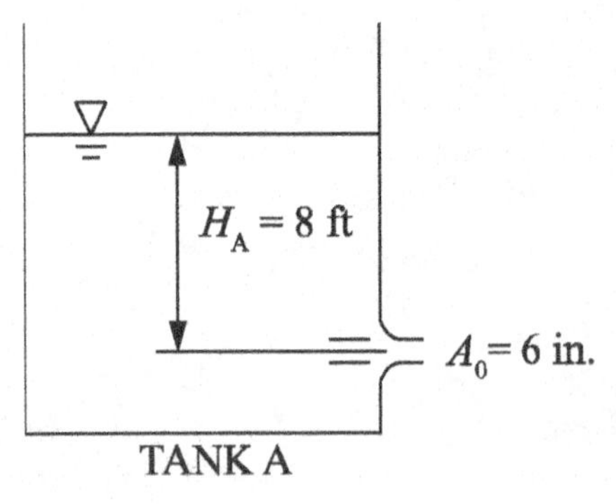

Discharge Velocity (ft/sec)

13.6
11.8
14.3
15.2
16.7

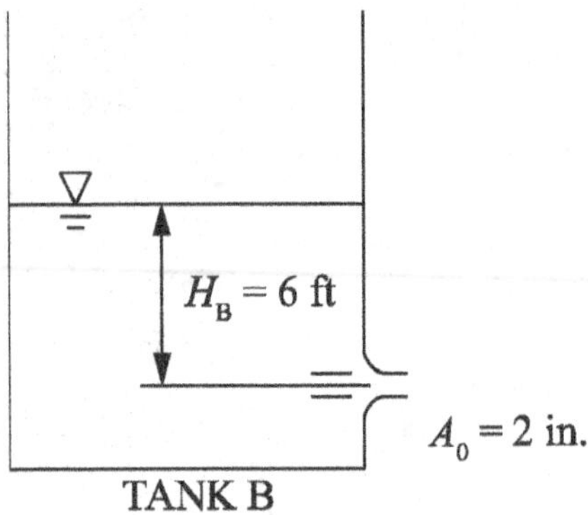

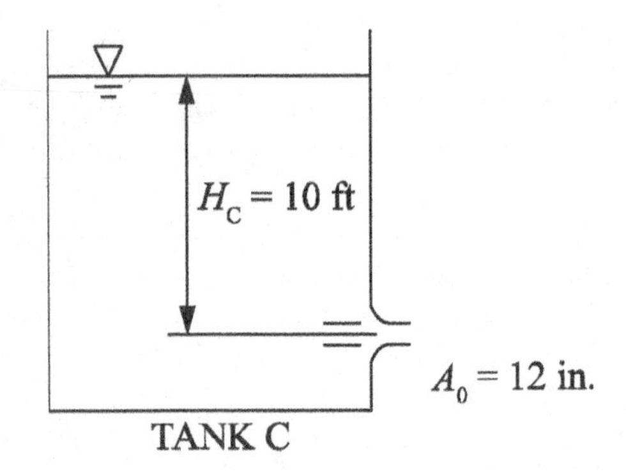

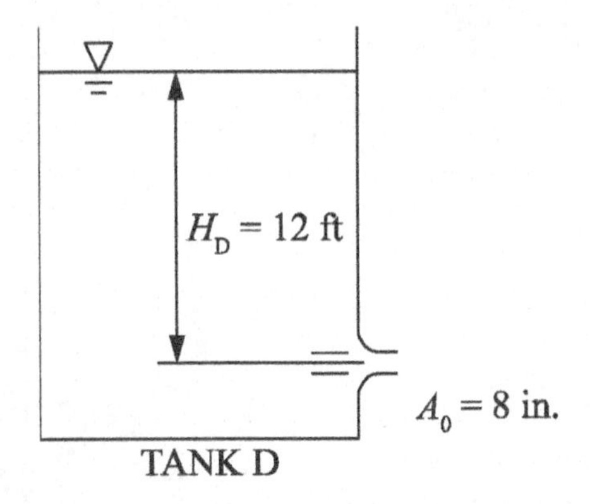

Copyright © 2020 by NCEES

48. The value of angle A in the figure is most nearly:

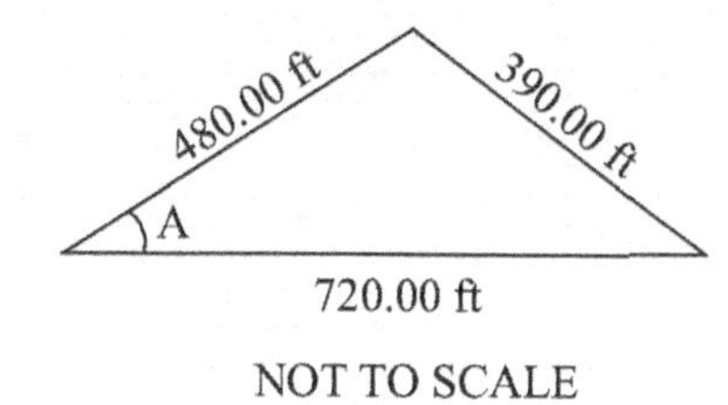

- ○ A. 30° 18' 47"
- ○ B. 32° 47' 50"
- ○ C. 39° 05' 38"
- ○ D. 42° 35' 09"

49. The area inside the quadrilateral, PC, PI, PT, and O, equals 83,164 ft^2. The shaded area (ft^2) between the circular curve and the tangents is most nearly:

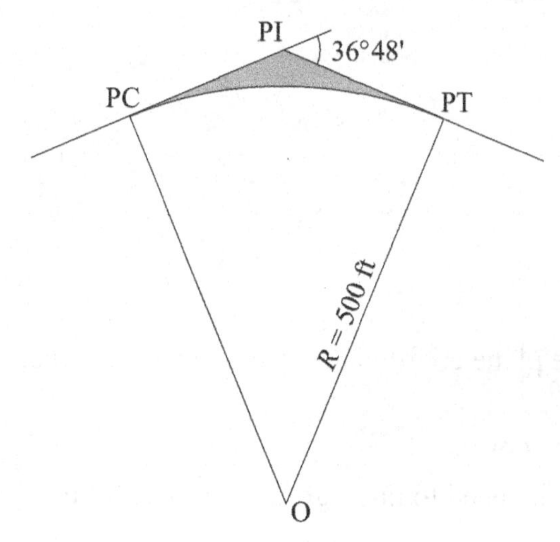

- ○ A. 2,879
- ○ B. 3,577
- ○ C. 5,407
- ○ D. 8,286

Copyright © 2020 by NCEES

50. The cross-sectional areas to be excavated (cut) at certain sections of a road project are as follows:

Station	Area (ft^2)
3+00	247
4+00	269
4+35	322
5+00	395
5+65	418
6+00	293
7+00	168

Using the prismoidal method, the volume of earth to be excavated (yd^3) between Stations 4+35 and 5+65 is most nearly:

- ○ A. 1,460
- ○ B. 1,840
- ○ C. 1,860
- ○ D. 1,900

51. The term *projected* as it relates to the state plane coordinate system means that the:

- ○ A. survey is inaccurate and needs to be corrected
- ○ B. survey points from found monuments need to undergo a unit conversion
- ○ C. handwritten coordinates are entered into computer software
- ○ D. earth's curvature needs to be taken into account for survey calculations

Copyright © 2020 by NCEES

52. A total station is set up 5.00 ft above a benchmark that has an elevation of 820.50 ft. A slope angle and slope distance of –3°15′ and 645.90 ft, respectively, are measured to a reflector that is set up 4.25 ft above a hub at Point B. Neglecting curvature and refraction, the elevation (ft) of the hub at Point B is most nearly:

- A. 785.76
- B. 784.63
- C. 783.88
- D. 779.63

53. A backsight of 7.76 ft is taken on a turning point with an elevation of 2,325.58 ft. If the foresight taken on the top of a construction pin is 4.25 ft, the elevation (ft) of the top of the pin is most nearly:

- A. 2,313.57
- B. 2,322.07
- C. 2,329.09
- D. 2,337.59

54. A 20-acre parcel of land has a rainfall intensity of 1.5 in./hr and a rational method runoff coefficient C of 0.10. The flow rate (cfs) for this site is most nearly:

- A. 3.0
- B. 5.0
- C. 7.5
- D. 9.0

Copyright © 2020 by NCEES

55. A flow of 15.5 cfs enters the pipe system at A as shown, and exits at B and C. Pipe data are given in the following table.

Pipe	f	Length (ft)	Diameter (in.)	Velocity (fps)
AB	0.03	200	24	2.0
AC	0.03	200	36	1.3
CB	0.03	200	48	

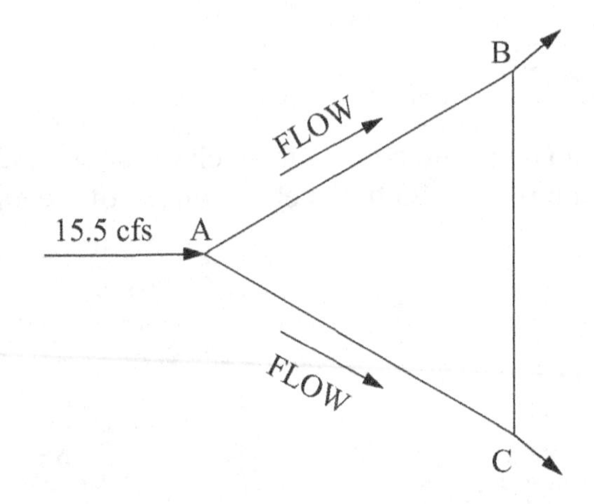

Assume the pipes are all at the same elevation. The head loss (ft) in Pipe CB is most nearly:

- A. 0.05
- B. 0.13
- C. 0.18
- D. 0.23

56. A pump station delivers wastewater from a sump at an elevation of 78 ft to a maintenance hole with a water surface elevation of 112 ft. The static head (ft) for this pump is most nearly:

- A. 17
- B. 34
- C. 44
- D. 78

Copyright © 2020 by NCEES

57. A 24-in. water distribution pipeline carrying 15 cfs flow branches at Point A into two pipelines, 1 and 2, both with Hazen-Williams *C* of 130. Pipeline 1 has an 18-in. diameter and is 2,400 ft long. Pipeline 2 has a 12-in. diameter and is 1,200 ft long. The branched pipes join at Point B to a 24-in. pipe to carry the flow downstream. The flow (cfs) in Pipeline 1 is most nearly:

- ○ A. 5.0
- ○ B. 10.0
- ○ C. 12.9
- ○ D. 15.0

58. A suppressed rectangular weir rises from the bottom of the pond to an elevation of 37 ft. The water is 50 ft deep, and the weir is 200 ft long. The flow (ft^3/sec) of water over the spillway is most nearly:

- ○ A. 1,500
- ○ B. 12,500
- ○ C. 23,800
- ○ D. 31,200

Copyright © 2020 by NCEES

59. For a new development of 75 acres (0.117 mi^2), the peak runoff for a 25-yr storm of 360 ft^3/s is to be limited to 180 ft^3/s through the use of a detention basin. Runoff Q is 3.4 in. Assume Type II rainfall. Using the TR-55 Method and figure below, the preliminary estimate of the storage volume (ac-ft) is most nearly:

Approximate Detention Basin Routing for Rainfall Types I, IA, II, and III

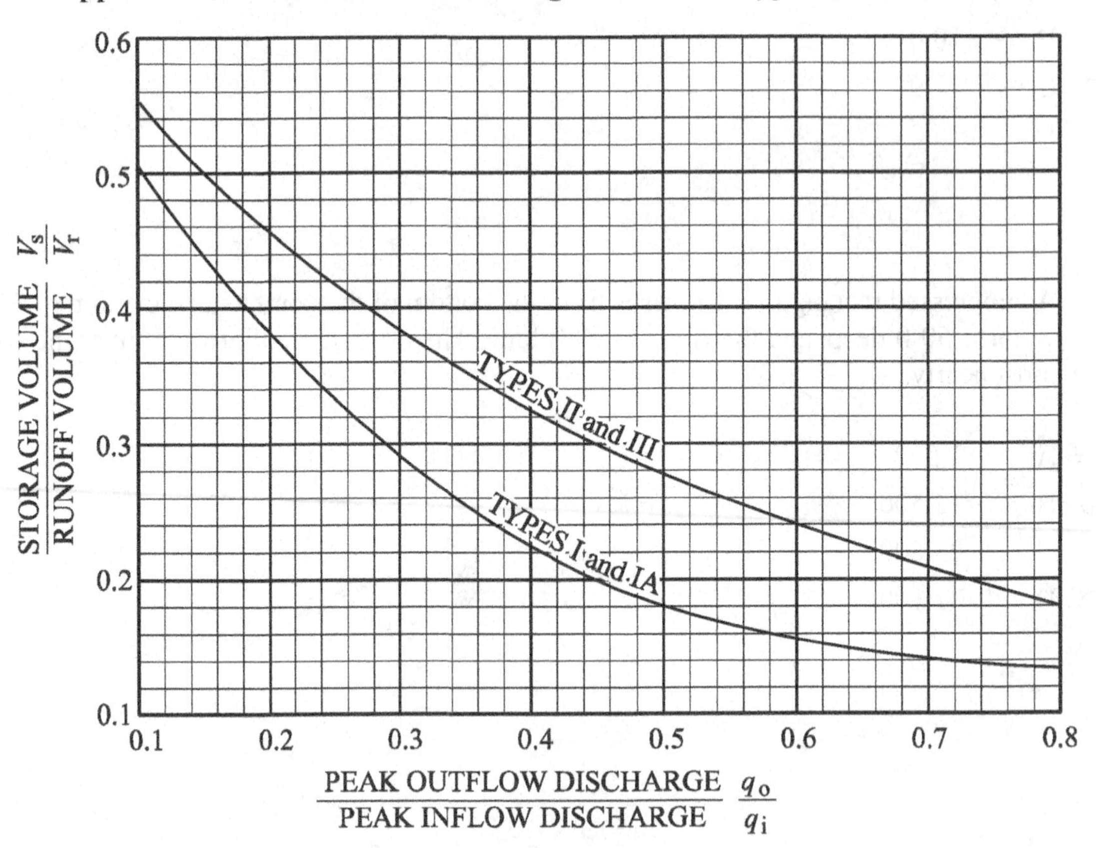

Urban Hydrology for Small Watersheds TR-55, U.S. Department of Agriculture, National Resource Conservation Service, June 1986.

- ○ A. 0.07
- ○ B. 0.11
- ○ C. 3.80
- ○ D. 5.94

Copyright © 2020 by NCEES

60. A 36-in-diameter sewer is installed at a slope of 0.006 ft/ft. Assuming the roughness coefficient n is constant with depth and equal to 0.015, the velocity (ft/sec) of water in a half-full pipe is most nearly:

- A. 4.3
- B. 5.8
- C. 6.3
- D. 10.1

61. Four monitoring wells—A, B, C, and D—lie equidistant (200 ft) from a fifth well, E. The depth to the water table is measured at each well and is shown below. The datum for the top of the casing is equal for the five wells. Groundwater flow moves in which direction from Point E?

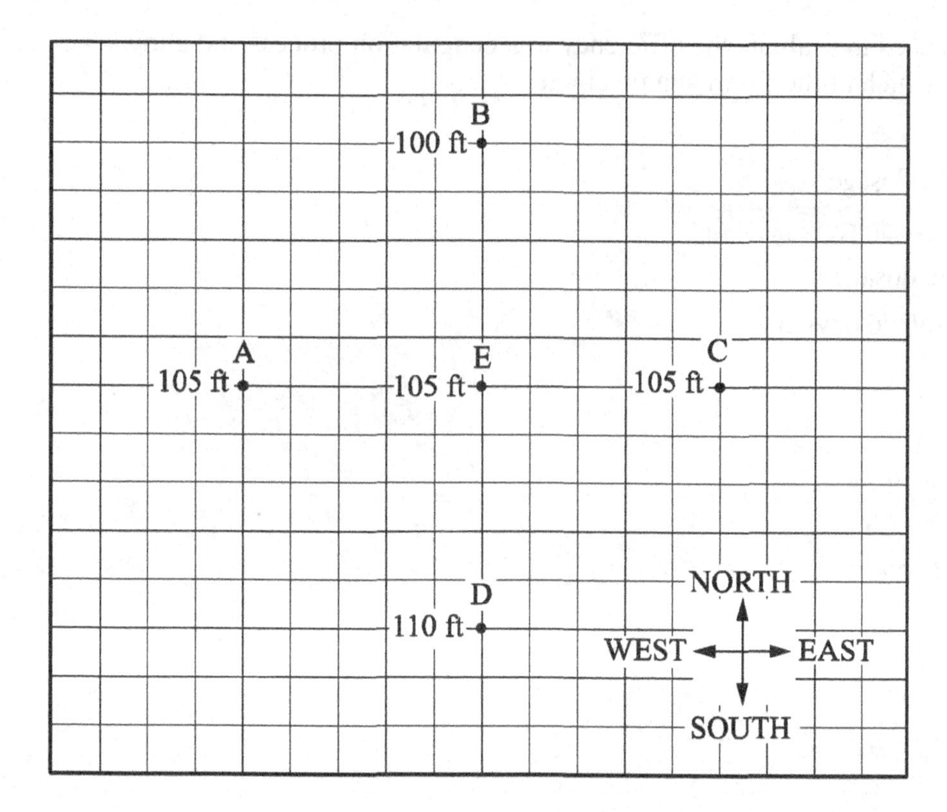

- A. South
- B. East
- C. North
- D. West

Copyright © 2020 by NCEES

62. Water quality characteristics can be categorized in four different ways. Match the provided characteristic with an appropriate category.

Water Quality Category	Characteristic
Physical	Hardness
Chemical	Odor
Microbiological	Radon
Radiological	*Giardia*
	Lead
	Turbidity

63. A jar test is used to evaluate the efficiency of a coagulation process and allows the plant operator to optimize which of the following parameters?

- ○ A. Alum dosage
- ○ B. Temperature
- ○ C. Lime dosage
- ○ D. Dissolved oxygen

Copyright © 2020 by NCEES

64. A concentrated load of 20 kips moves through the truss shown. Neglecting the weight of the truss, the maximum force (kips) in Member CD due to the moving load is most nearly:

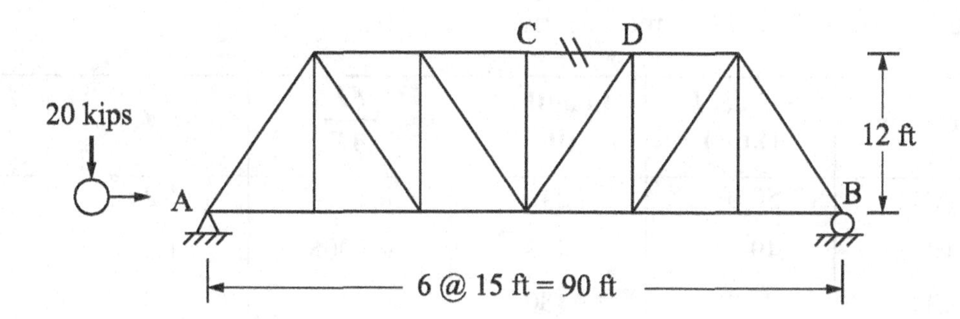

- A. 12.5
- B. 25
- C. 37.5
- D. 50

Copyright © 2020 by NCEES

65. The 40-kip vertical load at Joint C in the steel truss shown below produces the forces given in the accompanying table. The cross-sectional area of each member is 4.0 in^2, and the length of each member is given in the table. The elastic modulus of steel is 29,000 ksi. The downward vertical displacement (in.) of Joint C is most nearly:

Member	Force, F (kips)	Length, L (in.)	$\frac{FL}{AE}$	f	$f \cdot \frac{FL}{AE}$
AB	50.0	240	0.1034	1.25	0.1292
BC	49.2	473	0.2008	1.231	0.2472
CD	–75.0	480	–0.3103	–1.875	0.5818
AD	–30.0	288	–0.0745	–0.75	0.0559
BD	–25.0	240	–0.0517	–0.625	0.0323

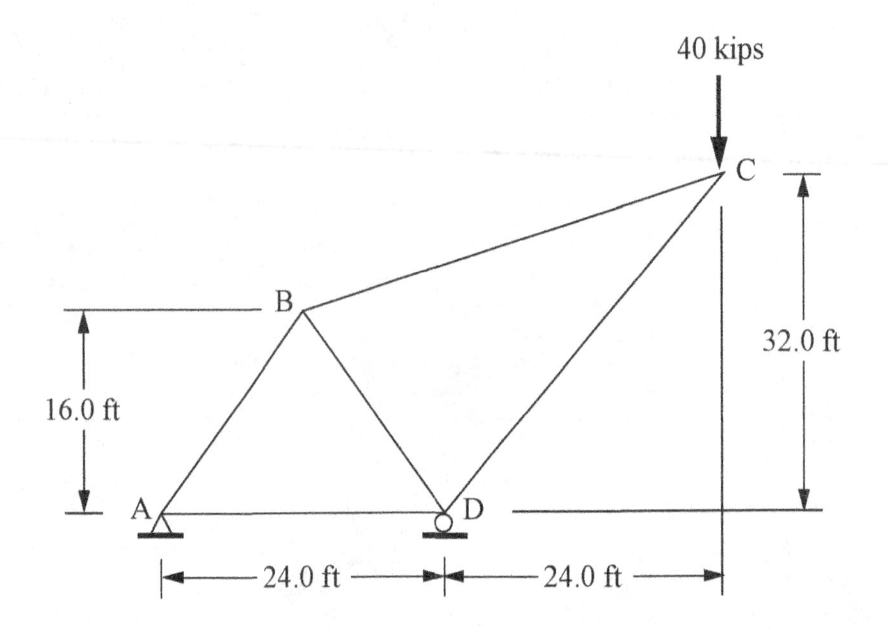

- ○ A. 1.046
- ○ B. 0.294
- ○ C. 0.132
- ○ D. 0.102

Copyright © 2020 by NCEES

66. The proportional limit and modulus of elasticity for a material are 40 ksi and 30,000 ksi, respectively. A square column made from this material has a moment of inertia equal to 6.8 $in.^4$ and an area equal to 9 in^2. Assume a pin-pin connected column so that the effective length factor K is equal to 1.0. The **maximum** column length (in.) based on the Euler formula is most nearly:

- O A. 42.2
- O B. 74.8
- O C. 195.0
- O D. 224.3

67. The frame in the figure below is:

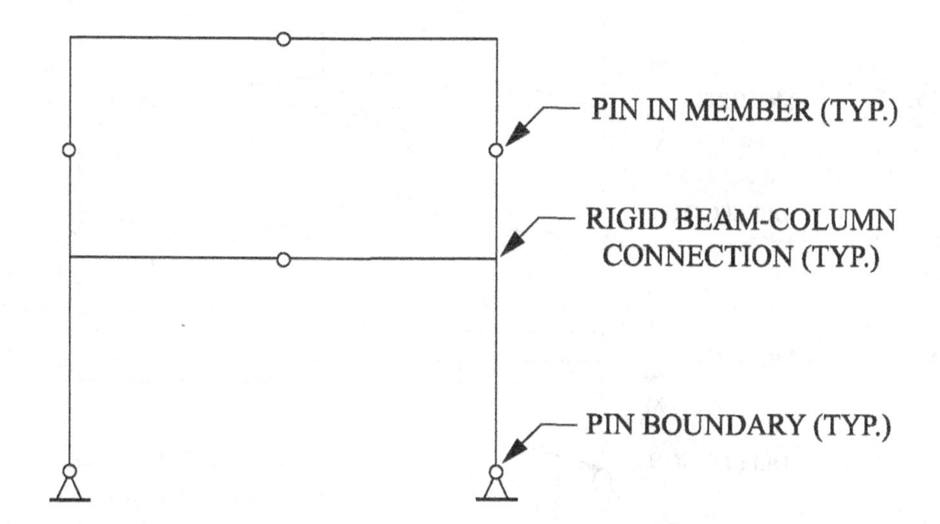

- O A. unstable
- O B. stable and determinate
- O C. indeterminate one degree
- O D. indeterminate two degrees

Copyright © 2020 by NCEES

68. Which combination of moment diagram and deflection shape most accurately corresponds to the continuous beam with loading shown?

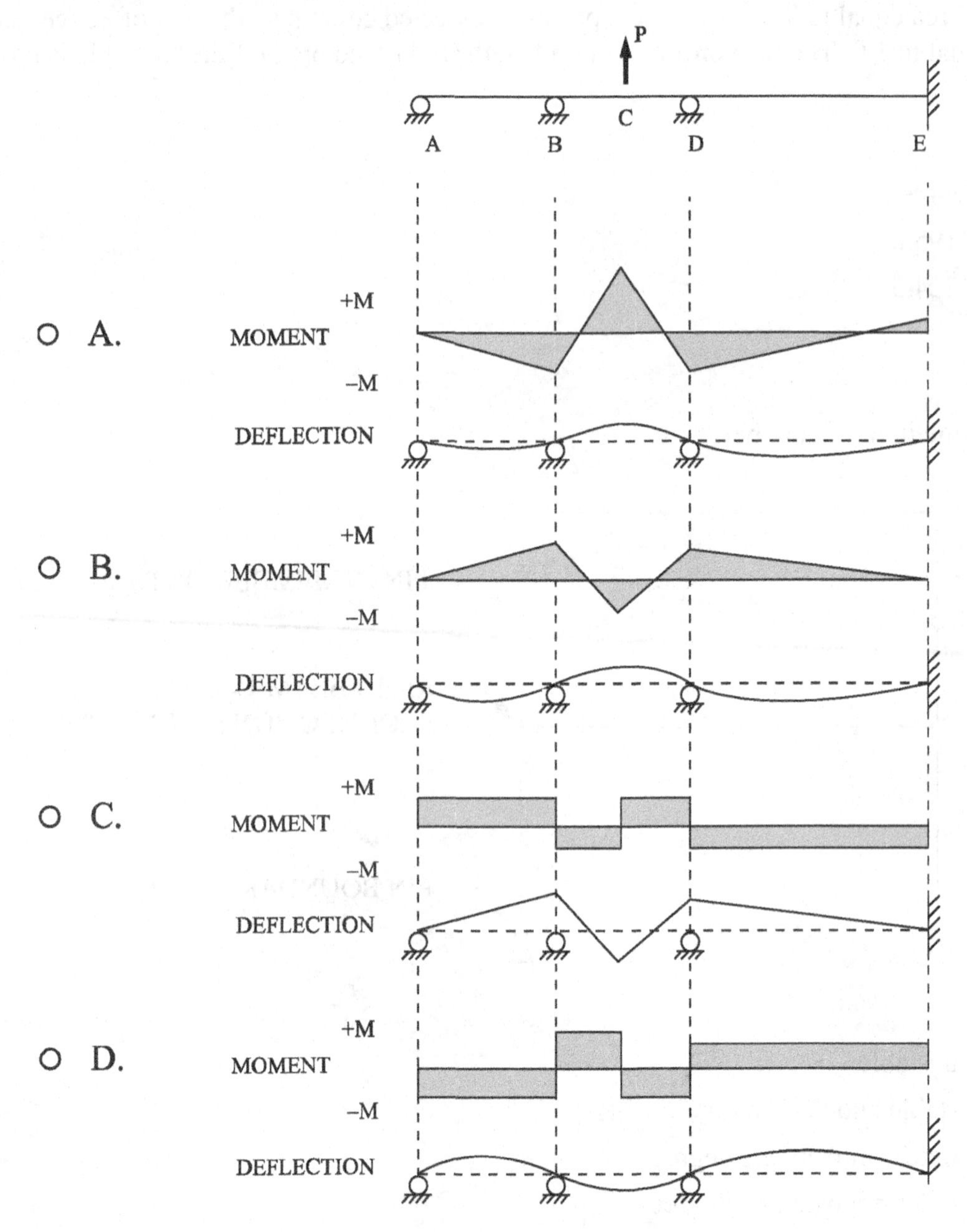

69. Which of the vertical-load influence lines shown below is correct for Member U_2U_3 of the truss shown below?

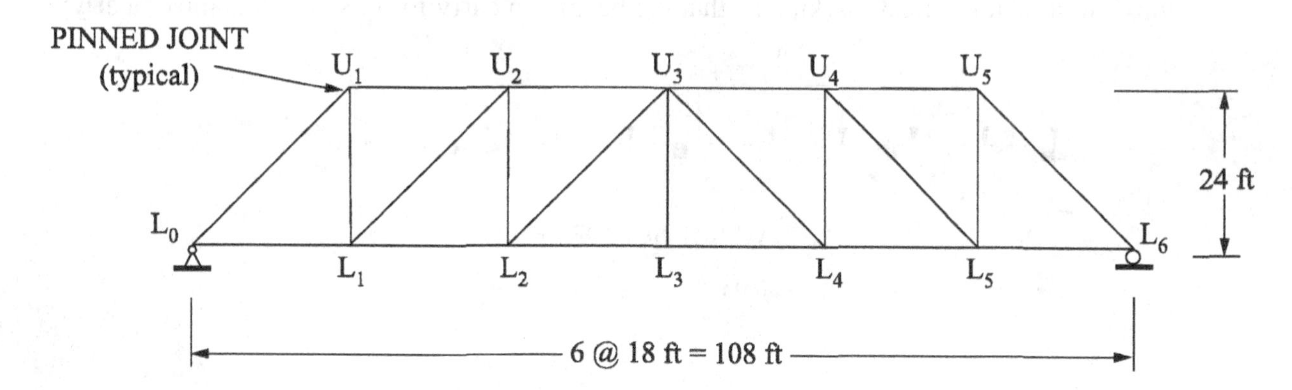

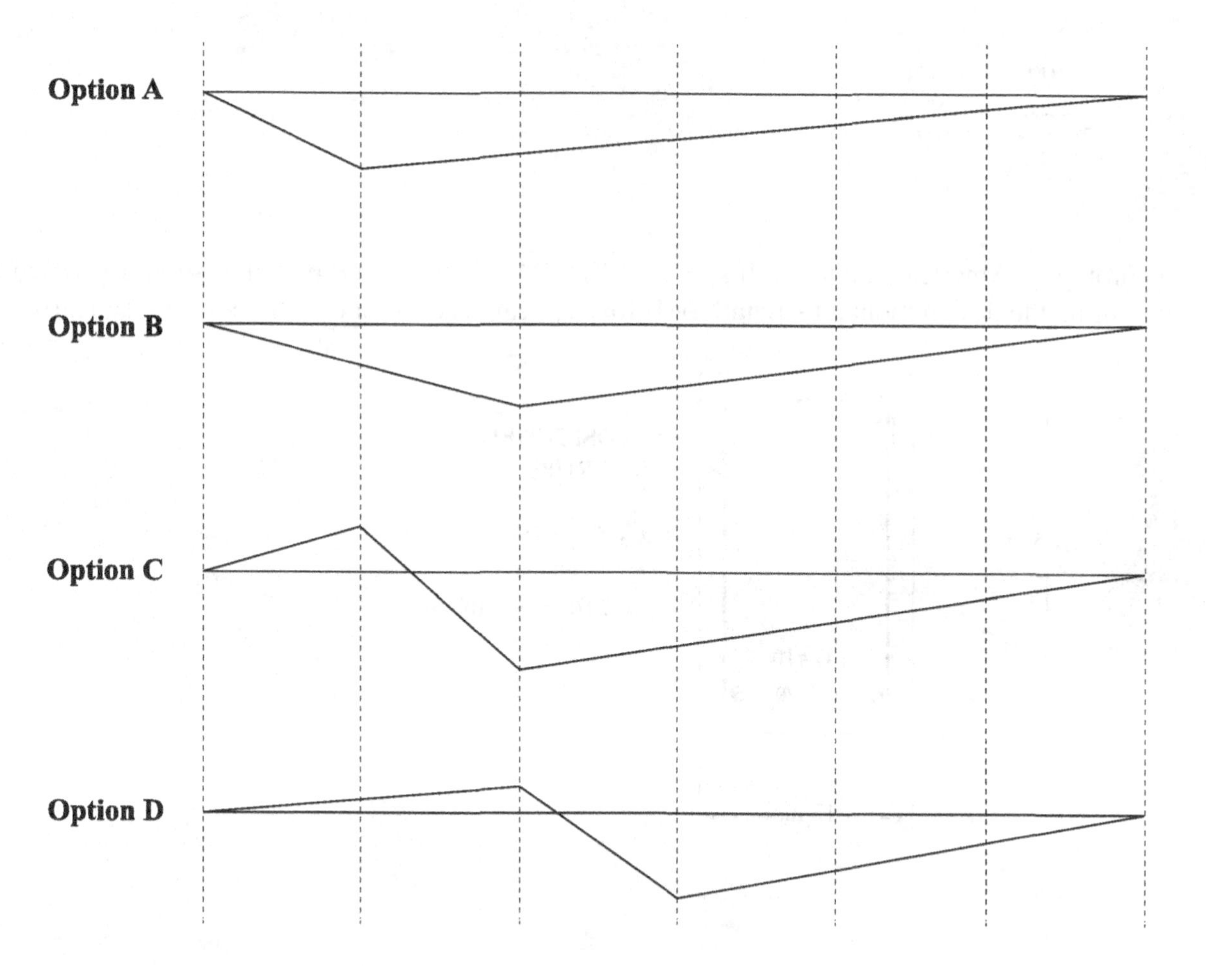

- ○ A. Option A
- ○ B. Option B
- ○ C. Option C
- ○ D. Option D

Copyright © 2020 by NCEES

70. The W21 × 57 steel beam shown in the figure has its compression flange laterally braced at the one-third points over its full length. Assume $F_y = 50$ ksi and $C_b = 1.0$ for the critical segment. The maximum factored load w_u (kips/ft) that the beam can carry for this length is most nearly:

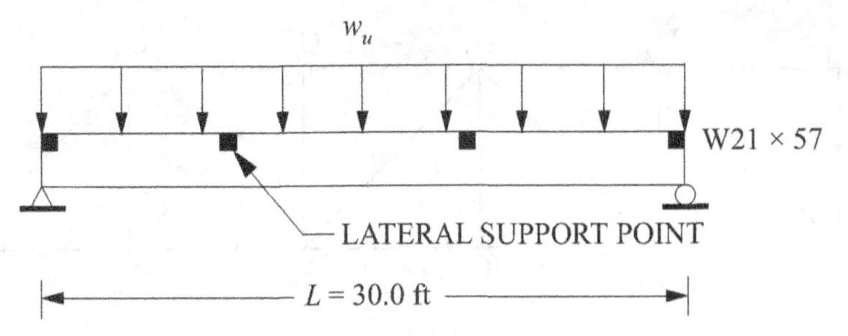

- ○ A. 2.658
- ○ B. 3.360
- ○ C. 4.302
- ○ D. 4.778

71. According to American Concrete Institute (ACI) 318-11, the value of ϕ that should be used in computing the design moment strength ϕM_n for the beam section shown below is most nearly:

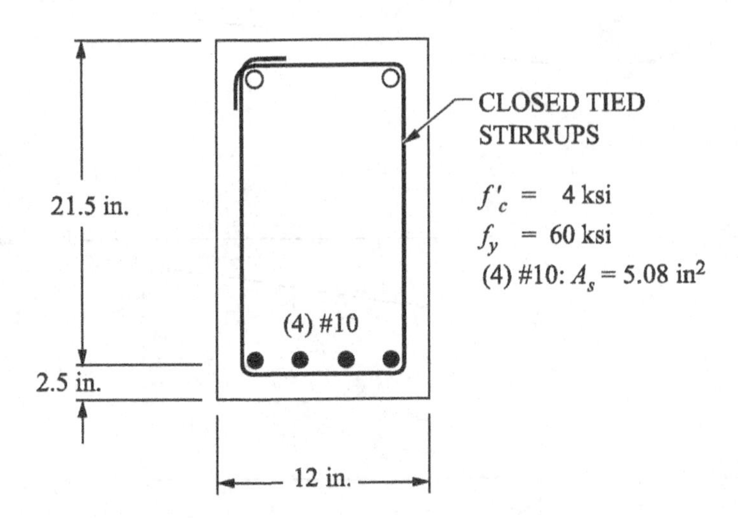

- ○ A. 0.80
- ○ B. 0.81
- ○ C. 0.84
- ○ D. 0.90

Copyright © 2020 by NCEES

72. In the truss shown, there is a pin connecting the members at each joint. The force (kips) in Member CD is most nearly:

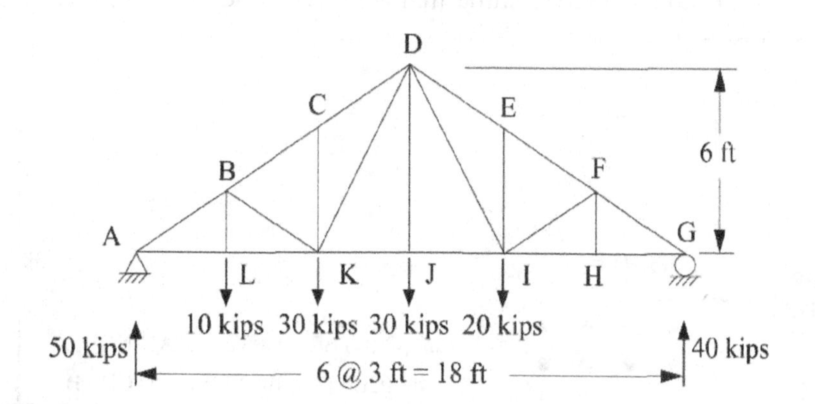

- A. –81 (compression)
- B. –113 (compression)
- C. –122 (compression)
- D. –169 (compression)

Copyright © 2020 by NCEES

73. A reinforced concrete beam is subjected to a factored moment $M_u = 648$ ft-kips. For concrete, $f'_c = 4{,}000$ psi. For steel, $f_y = 60{,}000$ psi. The beam is reinforced with eight #8 bars in two rows, positioned as shown in the figure. Assume that $\phi = 0.90$. The minimum adequate overall width b for this beam is most nearly:

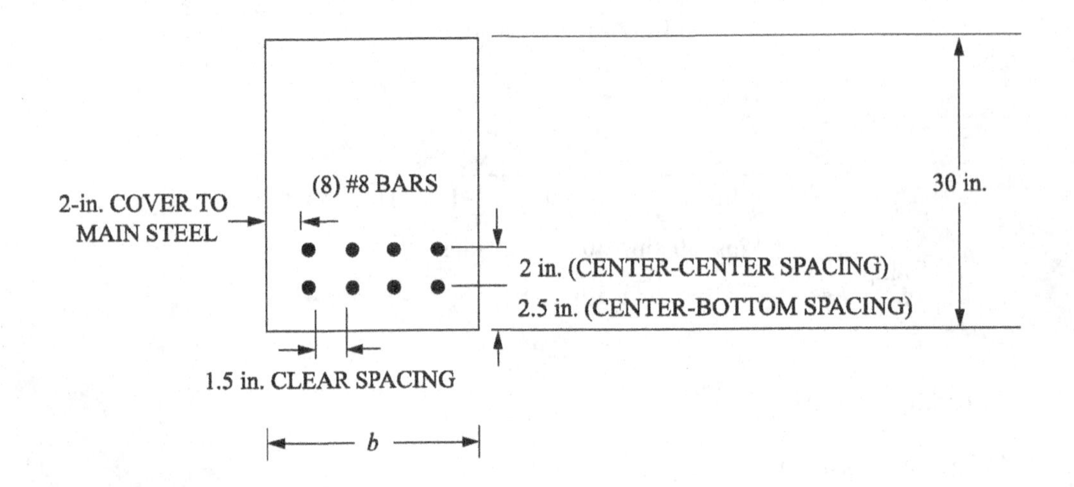

- ○ A. 10
- ○ B. 12
- ○ C. 13
- ○ D. 15

Copyright © 2020 by NCEES

74. Mark the area of the Atterberg chart provided that is associated with an elastic silt.

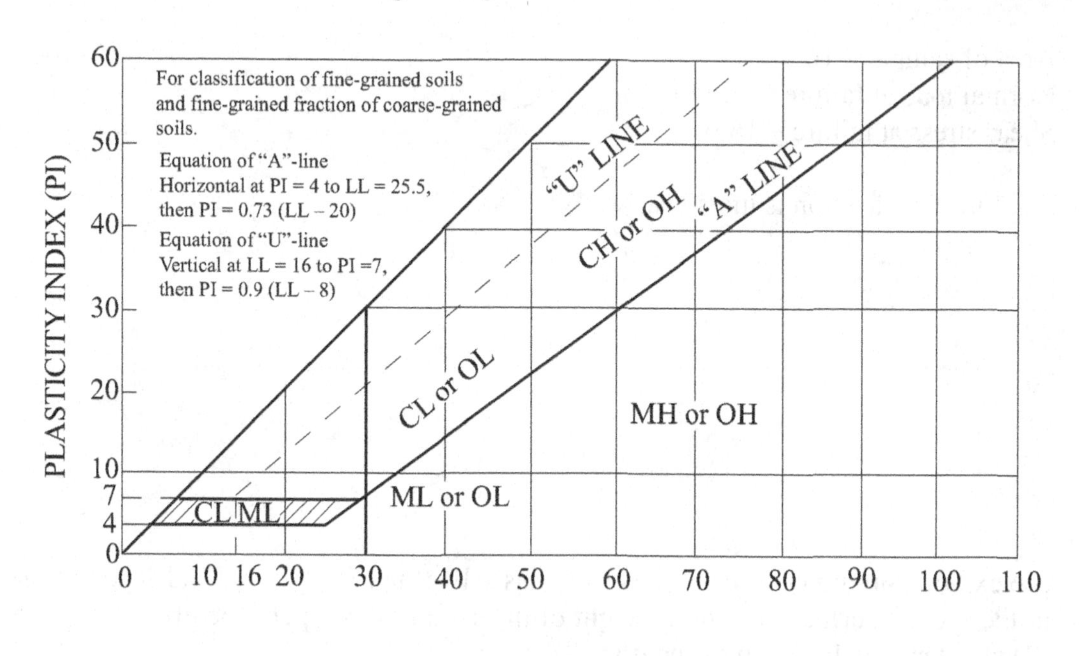

75. An undisturbed sample of soil has a specific gravity of solids of 2.70, a moisture content of 10.5%, and a void ratio of 0.63. The degree of saturation is most nearly:

- ○ A. 25%
- ○ B. 45%
- ○ C. 65%
- ○ D. 85%

76. Direct shear test data of a sand are shown below:

Area of sample = 16 in^2
Normal load at failure = 512 lb
Shear stress at failure = 16 psi

The angle of internal friction is most nearly:

- ○ A. 0°
- ○ B. 27°
- ○ C. 30°
- ○ D. 63°

77. Subsurface exploration indicates that a level site has a 10-ft upper layer of sand. The groundwater table is at the ground surface. The unit weight of the sand is 135.0 pcf. The effective overburden stress (psf) at a depth of 10 ft is most nearly:

- ○ A. 625
- ○ B. 725
- ○ C. 1,350
- ○ D. 1,975

78. A 12-ft-high retaining wall has backfill of granular soil with an angle of internal friction of 30° and a unit weight of 125 pcf. The resultant Rankine active force (lb/ft) on the wall is most nearly:

- ○ A. 2,250
- ○ B. 3,000
- ○ C. 9,000
- ○ D. 27,000

Copyright © 2020 by NCEES

NEXT→

79. A consolidated, undrained triaxial shear test was performed on an overconsolidated clay mix specimen with a diameter of 1.4 in. The test yielded a cohesion of 530 psf and an angle of internal friction of 18°. If the normal load at failure was 125 lb, the shear strength (psi) of the soil is most nearly:

- ○ A. 10
- ○ B. 26
- ○ C. 30
- ○ D. 556

80. A strip footing having a width $B = 2$ ft is to be constructed at ground surface ($D_f = 0$). Underlying the footing is sand having the following bearing capacity factors: $N_c = 0$, $N_\gamma = 25$, and $N_q = 20$. The unit weight of sand $\gamma = 120$ pcf. The ultimate bearing capacity q_{ult} (psf) of the footing is most nearly:

- ○ A. 1,200
- ○ B. 2,400
- ○ C. 3,000
- ○ D. 4,800

81. A three-story concrete building will be constructed on a vacant parcel in a city. The soil boring log shows a 20-ft-thick layer of loose soil over a 5-ft-thick limestone layer. Which of the following foundations will provide the least settlement for this building?

- ○ A. Spread footings
- ○ B. Mats foundation
- ○ C. Deep foundation
- ○ D. Wall foundation

Copyright © 2020 by NCEES

82. A normally consolidated 10-ft clay layer is surcharged, which causes a decrease in thickness. The coefficient of consolidation is 0.16 ft^2 per day and the time factor is 1.2 for $U = 50\%$. The clay layer is confined between two layers of dense sand. The time (days) required for 50% consolidation is most nearly:

- ○ A. 5
- ○ B. 38
- ○ C. 188
- ○ D. 750

83. A slope of clay-mix material experiences failure along a 100-ft-long slip surface at an angle of 27°. The soil above the slip surface weighs 100 tons, has an angle of internal friction of 20°, and has a cohesion of 1.2 psi. The factor of safety at slope failure is mostly nearly:

- ○ A. 0.7
- ○ B. 0.9
- ○ C. 1.7
- ○ D. 381.3

Copyright © 2020 by NCEES

84. A highway profile is shown in the figure. If the design stopping sight distance is 600 ft, the driver's eye height above the roadway surface is 3.50 ft, and the height of an object in the roadway to be avoided by stopping is 1.00 ft, the minimum design length (ft) of the vertical curve is most nearly:

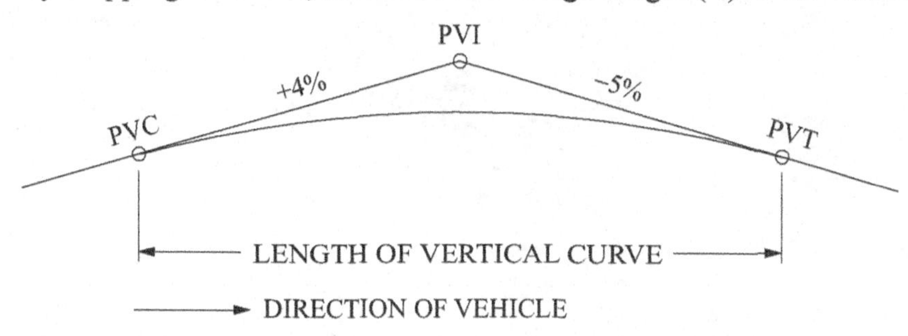

- ○ A. 3,600
- ○ B. 1,966
- ○ C. 1,136
- ○ D. 1,017

85. A flexible pavement system is to be designed using the AASHTO structural number design method with the following criteria:

Material	Minimum Thickness (in.)	Coefficient of Structural Layer
AC surfacing	2	0.44
Aggregate base	4	0.25
Aggregate subbase	4	0.10
Structural number = 2.50		

If the minimum thicknesses of the surfacing and aggregate base are used, the required thickness (in.) of the aggregate subbase is most nearly:

- ○ A. 4
- ○ B. 5
- ○ C. 6.5
- ○ D. 8.5

Copyright © 2020 by NCEES

86. A freeway lane has a volume of 1,400 vehicles/hr and an average vehicle speed of 45 mph. The time spacing (sec) between vehicles (center to center) is most nearly:

- ○ A. 2.6
- ○ B. 5.2
- ○ C. 15
- ○ D. 31

87. At an urban pedestrian crosswalk, the initial WALK signal is displayed for 6.0 sec, after which a flashing DON'T WALK signal is displayed. The pedestrian walking speed is 3.5 ft/sec, and the street to be crossed is 31.5 ft wide. At the end of the green time, the flashing DON'T WALK signal is terminated. The **minimum** length of time (sec) the green must be displayed is most nearly:

- ○ A. 6.0
- ○ B. 9.0
- ○ C. 12.5
- ○ D. 15.0

88. An urban intersection is being reconstructed to address safety problems, and it is estimated that the two mutually exclusive countermeasures have a crash reduction factor of 0.25 and 0.15, respectively. If the expected number of crashes per year is 10 and no significant growth in traffic is anticipated, the expected number of average crashes per year after reconstruction is most nearly:

- ○ A. 3.6
- ○ B. 4.0
- ○ C. 6.0
- ○ D. 6.4

Copyright © 2020 by NCEES

89. At two-way stop-controlled intersections, the sight distance required for minor street movements is determined by:

- ○ A. approach sight triangles
- ○ B. departure sight triangles
- ○ C. stopping sight distance
- ○ D. decision sight distance

90. For a given loading, soil conditions, and design life, which of the following pavement types will most likely be the thinnest highway pavement design?

- ○ A. Hot-mix asphalt
- ○ B. Warm-mix asphalt
- ○ C. Portland cement concrete
- ○ D. Composite hot-mix asphalt over Portland cement concrete

91. Which of the following statements about a basic freeway segment are true according to the *Highway Capacity Manual*?

Select **all** that apply.

- ☐ A. Freeway segments with 75-mph free-flow speed experience a reduction in operating speeds at a lower-volume threshold than a freeway segment with a 55-mph free-flow speed.
- ☐ B. The free-flow speed of a freeway segment is impacted by the amount of lateral clearance on the right side of the roadway.
- ☐ C. The capacity of a freeway segment with a 75-mph free-flow speed is higher than a similar facility with a 55-mph free-flow speed.
- ☐ D. A freeway segment with 13-ft lanes has higher free-flow speeds than a similar facility with 12-ft lanes.
- ☐ E. Increases in traffic volume lower the estimated operating speed of a freeway segment for both low- and high-volume ranges.

Copyright © 2020 by NCEES

92. To encourage more carpooling during the peak commute times, a metropolitan area is considering adding HOV lanes to a busy interstate segment. An existing transit route has a utility of –0.65, which is unaffected by the proposed change. If the existing non-HOV lanes have a utility of +1.2 and the proposed change introducing a carpool mode has a utility of –0.40, the percentage of trips expected to carpool is most nearly:

- ○ A. 0%
- ○ B. 15%
- ○ C. 17%
- ○ D. 74%

93. Operational manuals, warranties, guarantees, and as-built drawings are generally provided to the owner during which phase of the project?

- ○ A. Construction
- ○ B. Procurement
- ○ C. Close-out
- ○ D. Feasibility

94. A loader has a full-bucket capacity of 3 yd^3, and the average time required to place one bucketload of soil into a truck is 1 min. The loader is supported by four trucks with a volume of 15 yd^3 each and a cycle time of 12 min plus the time to load the truck. The ideal productivity (yd^3/hr) of this system is most nearly:

- ○ A. 180
- ○ B. 212
- ○ C. 277
- ○ D. 300

Copyright © 2020 by NCEES

95. A project has a CPI > 1.0 and an SPI < 1.0. This would indicate the project is:

- O A. behind schedule with a cost savings
- O B. ahead of schedule with a cost savings
- O C. behind schedule with a cost overrun
- O D. ahead of schedule with a cost savings

96. An embankment having a volume of 320,000 yd^3 is to be constructed from local borrow. The dry unit weight and moisture content of the borrow material were determined to be 106 pcf and 18.2%, respectively. The embankment material has a total unit weight of 122 pcf and a moisture content of 16.7%. The volume of borrow (yd^3) needed to construct the embankment is most nearly:

- O A. 274,100
- O B. 315,500
- O C. 324,500
- O D. 373,600

Copyright © 2020 by NCEES

97. Which set of orthographic views correctly represents the isometric view of the structure shown below?

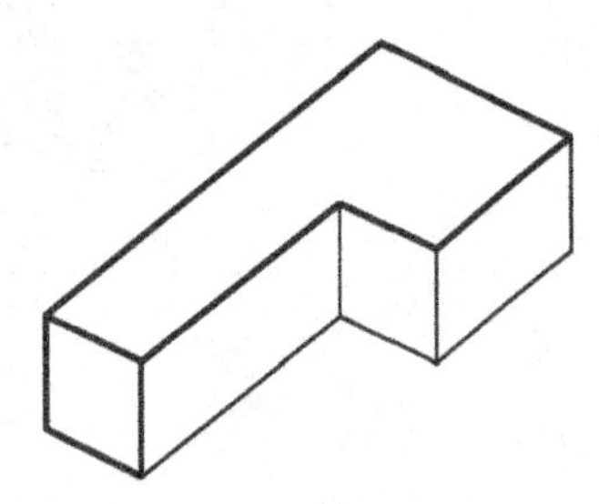

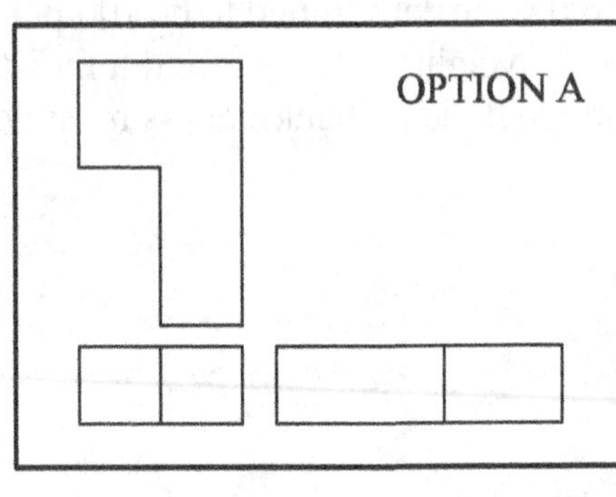

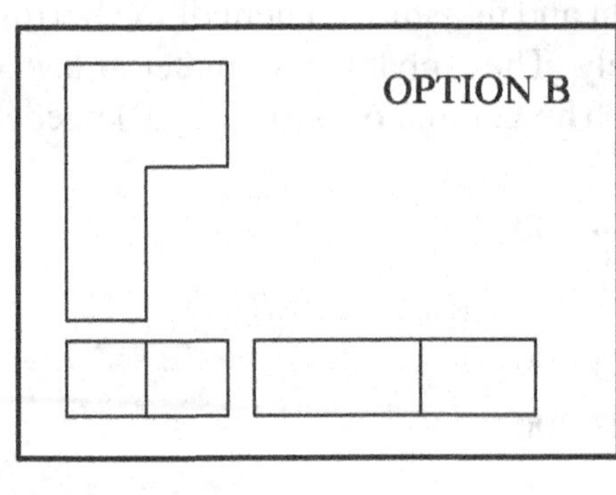

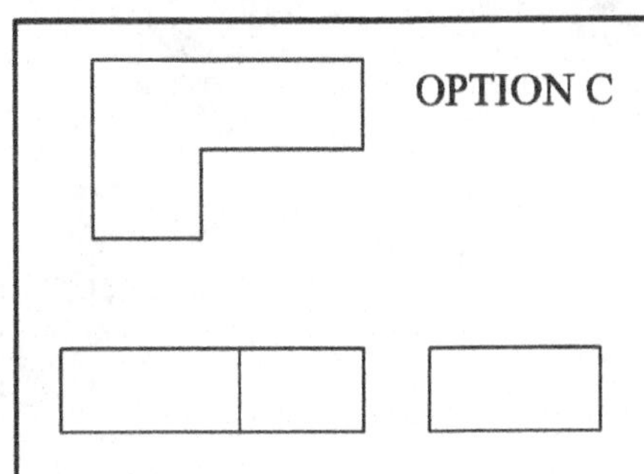

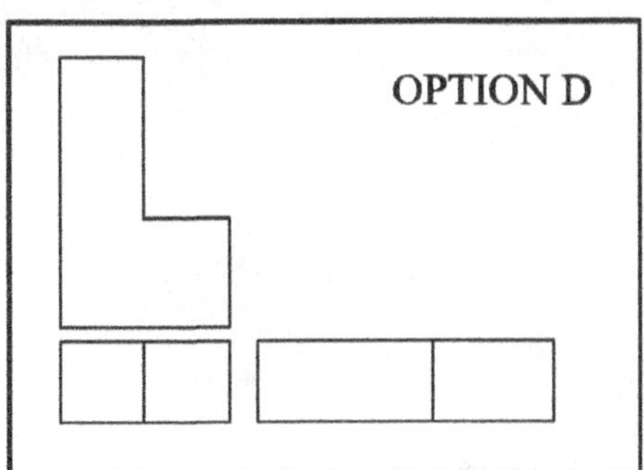

- ○ A. Option A
- ○ B. Option B
- ○ C. Option C
- ○ D. Option D

Copyright © 2020 by NCEES

98. The average production of the excavator is the controlling factor in a highway ditch-cleaning contract. Excavators with four different bucket sizes are available as rental units. The hourly rental rate is directly proportional to the bucket capacity of the excavator. Assume that production (loose yd^3/hr) is equal to (excavator cycles per hour) × (average bucket payload in LCY per cycle). The excavator characteristics are as follows:

Excavator	Minimum Cycle Time (min)	Average Bucket Payload (LCY)
1	0.25	0.50
2	0.33	1.00
3	0.50	1.75
4	0.58	2.00

The optimally efficient excavator is:

- A. Excavator 1
- B. Excavator 2
- C. Excavator 3
- D. Excavator 4

99. A work task has a current cost of $3,400, with a budget cost at this same point of $3,200. The total budget for this task is $4,000. The estimated cost at completion for this task is most nearly:

- A. $3,750
- B. $4,000
- C. $4,250
- D. $4,850

Copyright © 2020 by NCEES

100. A drawing of a roadway cross section is shown below. The arrow with a number indicates the:

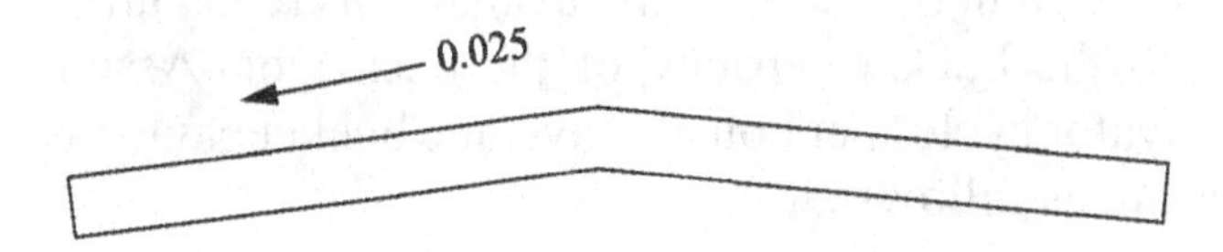

- ○ A. thickness of the surface coating is 0.025 in.
- ○ B. slope of the roadway is 3 in. per 10 ft across the slope
- ○ C. edge of the roadway will receive a chamfer of 1/4 in.
- ○ D. grooves ground into the surface of the roadway are 1/4 in. deep

Copyright © 2020 by NCEES

SOLUTIONS

FE CIVIL SOLUTIONS

Detailed solutions for each question begin on the next page.

1	C	26	C	51	D	76	B
2	D	27	A	52	B	77	B
3	A	28	C	53	C	78	D
4	B	29	D	54	A	79	C
5	A	30	D	55	B	80	C
6	C	31	B	56	B	81	C
7	D	32	C	57	B	82	C
8	A	33	B	58	D	83	B
9	C	34	B	59	D	84	B
10	C	35	A	60	C	85	C
11	A, E	36	A	61	A	86	A
12	A	37	C	62	see solution	87	D
13	B	38	D	63	A	88	D
14	B	39	D	64	C	89	B
15	B	40	B	65	A	90	C
16	C	41	D	66	B	91	B, C
17	C	42	D	67	B	92	B
18	A	43	A	68	B	93	C
19	C	44	D	69	B	94	A
20	see solution	45	C	70	B	95	A
21	A	46	C	71	C	96	B
22	B	47	see solution	72	A	97	B
23	D	48	A	73	D	98	C
24	D	49	A	74	see solution	99	C
25	D	50	C	75	B	100	B

FE CIVIL SOLUTIONS

1. Refer to the Integral Calculus section in the Mathematics chapter of the *FE Reference Handbook.*

$$A = \int_2^5 3x^2 dx = x^3 \Big|_2^5 = 5^3 - 2^3$$

$$= 117$$

THE CORRECT ANSWER IS: C

2. Refer to the Integral Calculus section in the Mathematics chapter of the *FE Reference Handbook.*

$$\int x^3 - x + 1 = \frac{x^4}{4} - \frac{x^2}{2} + x + C$$

THE CORRECT ANSWER IS: D

3. Refer to the Integral Calculus section in the Mathematics chapter of the *FE Reference Handbook.*

$$\int_2^4 \frac{1}{x^2} dx = -1\frac{1}{x}\Big|_2^4$$

$$= \left(-1\frac{1}{4}\right) - \left(-1\frac{1}{2}\right)$$

$$= \frac{1}{2} - \frac{1}{4}$$

$$= \frac{1}{4}$$

THE CORRECT ANSWER IS: A

Copyright © 2020 by NCEES

4. Refer to the Differential Calculus section in the Mathematics chapter of the *FE Reference Handbook.*

$y = 4x^3 + 3x^2z + 5xz^2 + 6z^3 + 20$, then $\left(\dfrac{\partial^2 y}{\partial x^2}\right) =$

$$\frac{\partial y}{\partial x} = 12x^2 + 6xz + 5z^2$$

$$\frac{\partial^2 y}{\partial x^2} = 24x + 6z$$

THE CORRECT ANSWER IS: B

5. Refer to the Dispersion, Mean, Median, and Mode Values section in the Engineering Probability and Statistics chapter of the *FE Reference Handbook.*

$$\text{Mean} = \frac{1}{N}\sum_{i=1}^{N} x_i = \frac{801}{9} = 89$$

95
91
90 ⎤
90 ⎥ Mode
Median [90 ⎦
88
87
85
85

The mean of the sample is 89. The median of the sample is 90. The mode of the sample is 90. Therefore, the median and the mode are equal.

THE CORRECT ANSWER IS: A

Copyright © 2020 by NCEES

6. Refer to the Vectors section in the Mathematics chapter of the *FE Reference Handbook.*

The cross product of vectors **A** and **B** is a vector perpendicular to **A** and **B**.

$$\begin{vmatrix} \mathbf{i} & \mathbf{j} & \mathbf{k} \\ 2 & 4 & 0 \\ 1 & 1 & -1 \end{vmatrix} = \mathbf{i}(-4) - \mathbf{j}(-2-0) + \mathbf{k}(2-4) = -4\mathbf{i} + 2\mathbf{j} - 2\mathbf{k}$$

To obtain a unit vector, divide by the magnitude.

$$\text{Magnitude} = \sqrt{(-4)^2 + 2^2 + (-2)^2} = \sqrt{24} = 2\sqrt{6}$$

$$\frac{-4\mathbf{i} + 2\mathbf{j} - 2\mathbf{k}}{2\sqrt{6}} = \frac{-2\mathbf{i} + \mathbf{j} - \mathbf{k}}{\sqrt{6}}$$

THE CORRECT ANSWER IS: C

7. Refer to the Engineering Probability and Statistics chapter of the *FE Reference Handbook.*

There is only one throw, 6 and 6, that sums to 12. There are 36 possible rolls of the dice. Therefore, 35/36 will have a sum less than 12.

$35/36 = 0.972$

THE CORRECT ANSWER IS: D

8. Refer to the t-Distribution section in the Engineering Probability and Statistics chapter of the *FE Reference Handbook.*

For a 99% confidence interval, $\alpha = 0.01 \rightarrow \alpha/2 = 0.005$.

Use Student's t-distribution with $\nu = 4$. Refer to the table, where $t_{0.005,4} = 4.604$.

Confidence interval = 23.2% ± 4.604% = (18.6%, 27.8%)

THE CORRECT ANSWER IS: A

Copyright © 2020 by NCEES

9. Refer to the Ethics chapter of the *FE Reference Handbook.*

Section B.1 in the Rules of Professional Conduct states: Licensees shall undertake assignments only when qualified by education or experience in the specific technical fields of engineering or surveying involved.

THE CORRECT ANSWER IS: C

10. Refer to the NCEES Rules of Professional Conduct in the Ethics chapter of the *FE Reference Handbook.*

Licensees may express a professional opinion publicly only when it is founded on adequate knowledge of the facts and a competent evaluation of the subject matter.

THE CORRECT ANSWER IS: C

11. Refer to the NCEES Rules of Professional Conduct, Section B, in the Ethics chapter of the *FE Reference Handbook.*

THE CORRECT ANSWERS ARE: A, E

12. *Black's Law Dictionary* defines *lien* as a claim on property for payment of debt. Examinees are expected to be familiar with liens.

THE CORRECT ANSWER IS: A

13. Refer to the capital recovery equation in the Engineering Economics chapter of the *FE Reference Handbook.*

$A = P\,(A/P,\ i\%,\ n)$

$= 100{,}000\,(A/P,\ 1\%,\ 60)$

$= 100{,}000\,(0.0222)$

$= \$2{,}220/\text{month}$

THE CORRECT ANSWER IS: B

Copyright © 2020 by NCEES

14. Refer to the cash flow formulas in the Engineering Economics chapter of the *FE Reference Handbook.*

Look at the present worth of each option.

The present worth values are all given by:

$$P = \text{First Cost} + \text{Annual Cost} \times (P/A, 12\%, 8) - \text{Salvage Value} \times (P/F, 12\%, 8)$$
$$= \text{First Cost} + \text{Annual Cost} \times 4.9676 - \text{Salvage Value} \times 0.4039$$

Then $P(\text{A}) = \$63{,}731$
$P(\text{B}) = \$63{,}392$
$P(\text{C}) = \$63{,}901$
$P(\text{D}) = \$63{,}222$

The cash flows are all costs, so the two most preferable pieces of equipment, those with the lowest present worth costs, are B and D, and the difference between them is $170.

THE CORRECT ANSWER IS: B

15. Refer to the Breakeven Analysis section in the Engineering Economics chapter of the *FE Reference Handbook.*

$1.50 (5,000) = $7,500

$0.50 (5,000) = $2,500

Annual savings = $7,500 – $2,500 = $5,000

Additional investment = $15,000 – $1,000 = $14,000

Payback period = $14,000/$5,000 = 2.8 years

THE CORRECT ANSWER IS: B

Copyright © 2020 by NCEES

16. Refer to the Probability Functions, Distributions, and Expected Values section in the Engineering Probability and Statistics chapter of the *FE Reference Handbook.*

$EV_{\text{purchase insurance}} = (C_1P_1) + (C_2P_2) + (C_3P_3)$

$EV_{\text{purchase insurance}} = (0.88 \times 0) + (0.11 \times \$800) + (0.01 \times \$1{,}000) = 0 + \$88 + \$10 = \$98$

Cost with annual insurance premium is \$2,000 + \$98 = \$2,098

$EV_{\text{not to purchase insurance}} = (C_1P_1) + (C_2P_2) + (C_3P_3)$

$EV_{\text{not to purchase insurance}} = (0.88 \times 0) + (0.11 \times \$800) + (0.01 \times \$100{,}000) = 0 + \$88 + \$1{,}000 = \$1{,}088$

Compare $EV_{\text{not to purchase insurance}}$ and $EV_{\text{to purchase insurance}}$

$EV_{\text{not to purchase insurance}} < EV_{\text{to purchase insurance}} = \$2{,}098 - \$1{,}088 =$ savings of \$1,010

THE CORRECT ANSWER IS: C

17. Refer to the Engineering Economics chapter of the *FE Reference Handbook.*

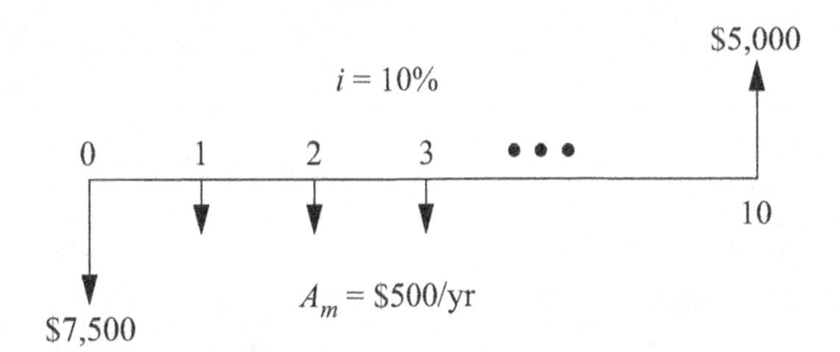

$$A = A_m + P\left(\frac{A}{P}, i, n\right) - SV\left(\frac{A}{F}, i, n\right)$$

$$= \$500 + \$7{,}500\left(\frac{A}{P}, 10\%, 10\right) - \$5{,}000\left(\frac{A}{F}, 10\%, 10\right)$$

$$= \$500 + \$7{,}500(0.16275) - \$5{,}000(0.06275)$$

$$= \$1{,}407 \text{ per year}$$

THE CORRECT ANSWER IS: C

Copyright © 2020 by NCEES

18. Refer to the Resolution of a Force section in the Statics chapter of the *FE Reference Handbook.*

$R_x = \sum F_{xi}, \qquad R_y = \sum F_{yi}, \qquad i = 1,2,3$

$R_x = 2.12 + 5\cos 105° = 2.12 - 1.29 = 0.83 \text{ N}$

$R_y = 2.12 + 5\sin 105° = 2.12 + 4.83 = 6.95 \text{ N}$

$R = \sqrt{R_x^{\ 2} + R_y^{\ 2}} = \sqrt{0.83^2 + 6.95^2} = 6.999 \text{ N}$

THE CORRECT ANSWER IS: A

19. Refer to the Systems of Forces section in the Statics chapter of the *FE Reference Handbook.*

Draw a free-body diagram.

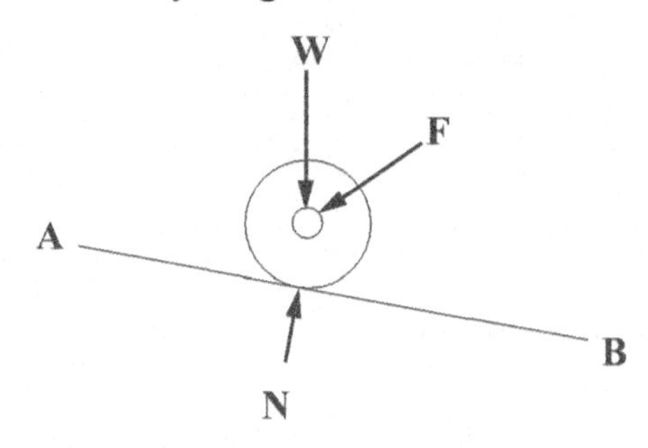

$\therefore$

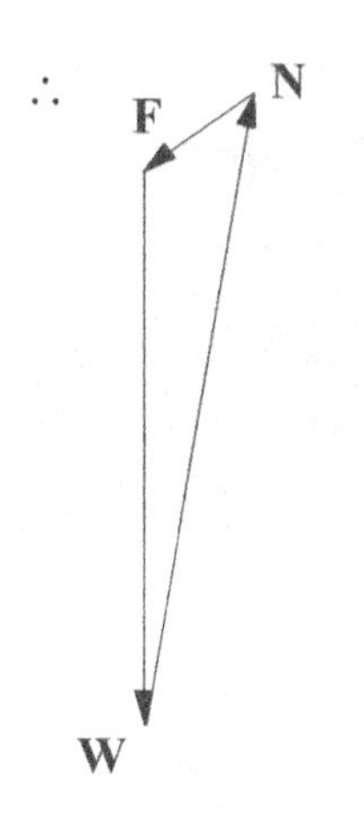

Since force Σ vectors = 0

THE CORRECT ANSWER IS: C

Copyright © 2020 by NCEES

20. Refer to the Systems of Forces section in the Statics chapter of the *FE Reference Handbook.*

$\Sigma F_x = 0 = -6 + \frac{3}{5}10$ Therefore, no additional *x*-force required

$\Sigma F_y = 0 \neq 6 - 10 + \frac{4}{5}10$ Therefore, additional *y*-force required

$\Sigma F_y = 0 = 6 - 10 + \frac{4}{5}10 + P_y$

$P_y = -4 \downarrow$

$\Sigma M_o = 0 = 6(5) - 10(3) + \frac{4}{5}10(6) - 4(x)$

$x = 12$

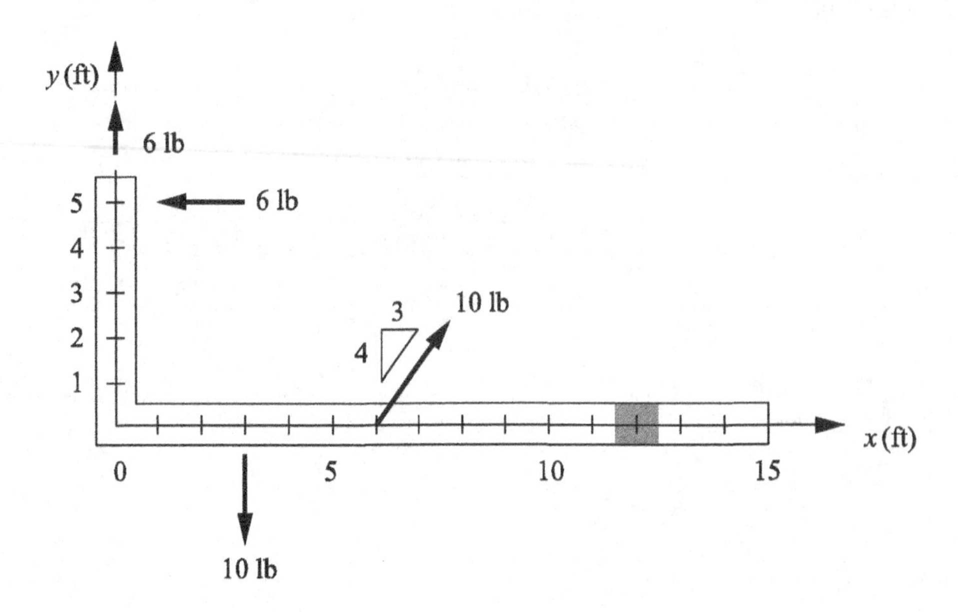

THE CORRECT ANSWER IS SHADED ABOVE.

Copyright © 2020 by NCEES

21. Refer to the Statically Determinant Truss section in the Statics chapter of the *FE Reference Handbook.*

Zero-force members usually occur at joints where members are aligned as follows:

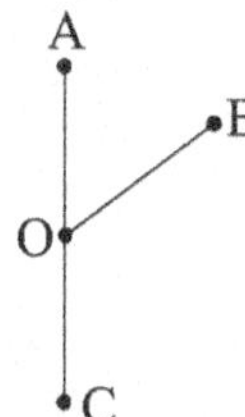

That is, joints where two members are along the same line (OA and OC) and the third member is at some arbitrary angle create a zero-force member. That member (OB) is a zero-force member because the forces in OA and OC must be equal and opposite.

For this specific problem, we immediately examine Joints B and E:

B:

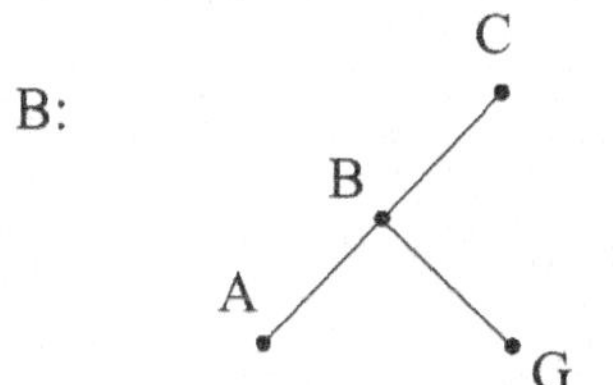

E:

D
C
E
F

BG is a zero-force member **CE is a zero-force member**

Now, examine Joint G. Since BG is zero-force member, the joint effectively looks like:

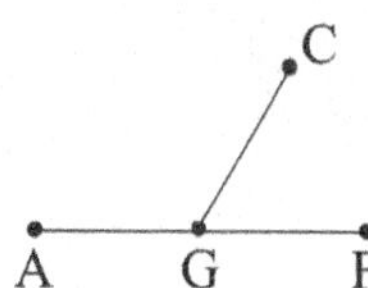

and, therefore, **CG** is another zero-force member.

Finally, examine Joint C. Since both CG and CE are zero-force members, the joint effectively looks like:

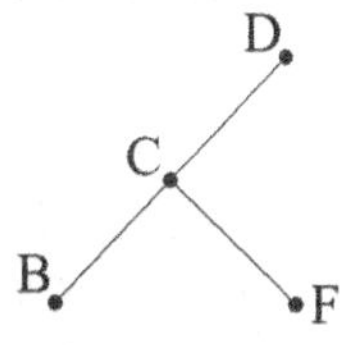

and, therefore, CF is another zero-force member. Thus, BG, CE, CG, and CF are the zero-force members.

THE CORRECT ANSWER IS: A

Copyright © 2020 by NCEES

22. Refer to the Centroids of Masses, Areas, Lengths, and Volumes section in the Statics chapter of the *FE Reference Handbook.*

The location of the centroid from the y-axis in the direction parallel to the x-axis is given by:

$$\bar{x} = \frac{1}{A}\int_A x dA \qquad \text{where } dA = (y_2 - y_1)\,dx$$

$$\bar{x} = \frac{\int_0^3 x\left(x - \frac{x^2}{3}\right)dx}{\int_0^3 \left(x - \frac{x^2}{3}\right)dx} \qquad \text{or} \qquad \bar{x} = \frac{\int_0^3 \left(x^2 - \frac{1}{3}x^3\right)dx}{\int_0^3 \left(x - \frac{1}{3}x^2\right)dx}$$

THE CORRECT ANSWER IS: B

23. Refer to the Moment of Inertia section in the Statics chapter of the *FE Reference Handbook.*

$I_{xc} = h^3(a^2 + 4ab + b^2)/36(a + b)$

$= 6^3[(3^2 + (4 \times 3 \times 6) + 6^2)]/[36 \times (3+6)]$
$= 78$

$A = h(a + b)/2$
$A = 6(3 + 6)/2 = 27$

$I_{x'} = I_{xc} + d_y^2 A$
$= 78 + (1.5^2)(27)$
$= 138.85$

THE CORRECT ANSWER IS: D

Copyright © 2020 by NCEES

24. Refer to the Friction section in the Statics chapter of the *FE Reference Handbook.*

Normal to the plane:

$\Sigma F_n = 0$: $N - mg \cos \phi = 0 \rightarrow N = mg \cos \phi$

Tangent to the plane:

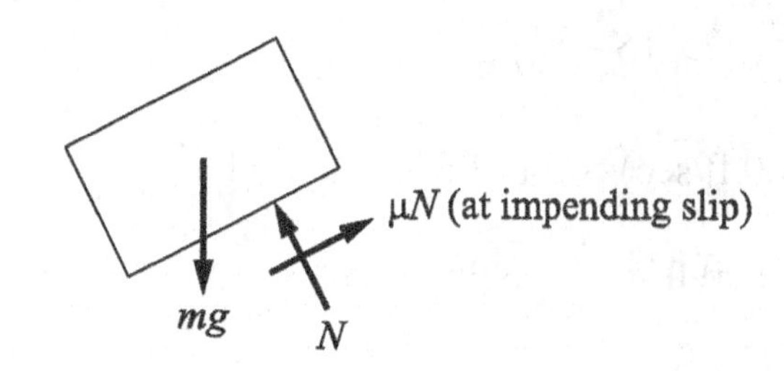

$\Sigma F_t = 0$: $-mg \sin \phi + \mu N = 0$

$\therefore -mg \sin \phi + \mu mg \cos \phi = 0$

$$\frac{\sin \phi}{\cos \phi} = \tan \phi = \mu$$

$\tan \phi = 0.25$

THE CORRECT ANSWER IS: D

25. $R_y = \Sigma F_y = \frac{12}{13}(260) + \frac{3}{5}(300) - 50 = 370$

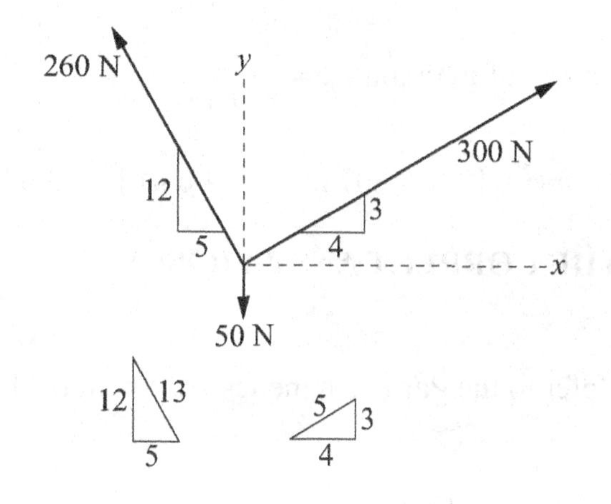

$R_x = \Sigma F_x = -\frac{5}{13}(260) + \frac{4}{5}(300) = 140$

$R = \sqrt{R_x^2 + R_y^2} = \sqrt{370^2 + 140^2}$

$R = 396$ N

THE CORRECT ANSWER IS: D

Copyright © 2020 by NCEES

26. Refer to the Constant Acceleration section in the Dynamics chapter of the *FE Reference Handbook.*

$$v^2 = v_o^2 + 2a_c(S - S_o)$$

$$v_o^2 = v^2 - 2a_c(S - S_o)$$

$= (60 \text{ ft/sec})^2 - 2\ (12 \text{ ft/sec}^2)(140 \text{ ft})$

$= 3{,}600 \text{ ft}^2/\text{sec}^2 - 3{,}360 \text{ ft}^2/\text{sec}^2$

$= 240 \text{ ft}^2/\text{sec}^2$

$v_o = 15.5$ ft/sec

THE CORRECT ANSWER IS: C

27. Refer to the Kinetics of a Rigid Body section in the Dynamics chapter of the *FE Reference Handbook.*

Radius of gyration $r_m = \sqrt{\dfrac{I}{m}}$

$I = mr^2 = [8 \text{ N}/9.807 \text{ m/s}^2 \times (4 \text{ cm})^2] = 13.0 \text{ kg}\cdot\text{cm}^2$

THE CORRECT ANSWER IS: A

28. Refer to the Particle Kinetics section in the Dynamics chapter of the *FE Reference Handbook.*

$F = ma$
(20 N) = (5 kg)(a)
$a = 4 \text{ m/s}^2$

$v = at$
18 m/s = 4 m/s² (t)
$t = 4.50$ s

THE CORRECT ANSWER IS: C

Copyright © 2020 by NCEES

29. Refer to the Impact section in the Dynamics chapter of the *FE Reference Handbook.*

Energy may or may not be conserved. It is conserved only if the coefficient of restitution is 1.00. Momentum is always conserved.

THE CORRECT ANSWER IS: D

30. Refer to the Beams section in the Mechanics of Materials chapter of the *FE Reference Handbook.*

$$\frac{10\text{ m}}{10\text{ kN}} = \frac{x}{6\text{ kN}}$$

$x = 6$ m

Area 1 = 13(2) = 26 kN·m

$$\text{Area } 2 = \frac{6(6)}{2} = 18\text{ kN·m}$$

Area 3 = 4(4) = 16 kN·m

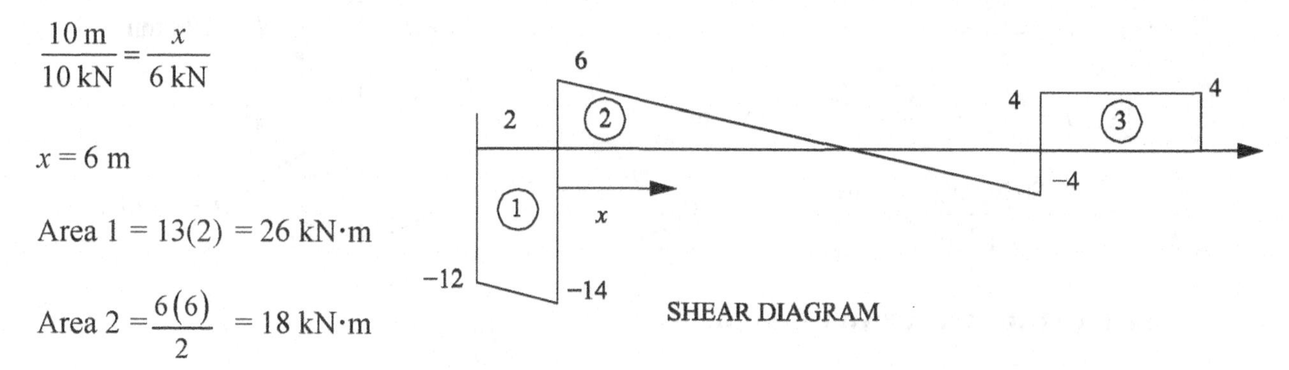

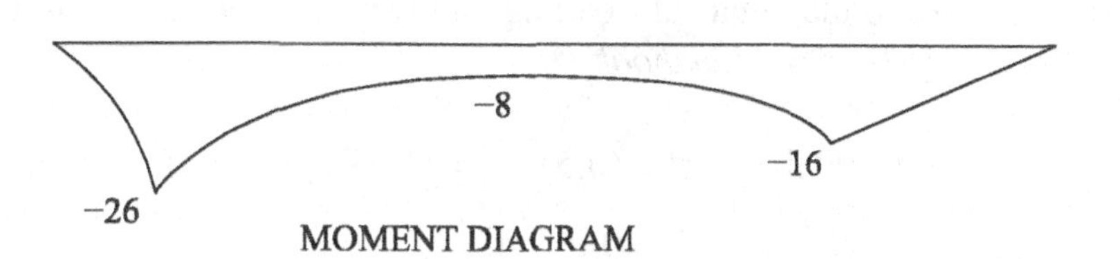

Maximum magnitude of the bending moment is 26 kN·m.

THE CORRECT ANSWER IS: D

Copyright © 2020 by NCEES

31. Refer to the Cylindrical Pressure Vessel section in the Mechanics of Materials chapter of the *FE Reference Handbook.*

The cylinder can be considered thin-walled if $\frac{t}{\frac{d_i}{2}} \le 0.10$. In this case, $t = 12$ mm and $d_i = 700$ mm.

Since $\frac{t}{\frac{d_i}{2}} = \frac{12}{350} = 0.034$ which is ≤ 0.10, the pipe is thin-walled.

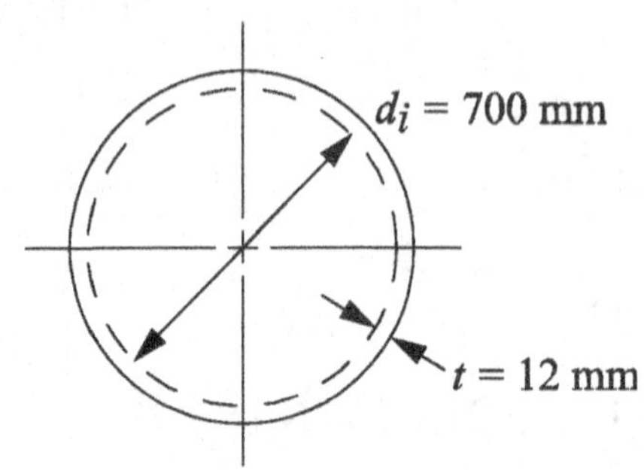

Thus $\sigma_t = \frac{P_i r}{t}$

where $r = \frac{r_i + r_o}{2} = \frac{350 + 362}{2} = 356 \text{ mm}$

$$\sigma_t = \frac{(1.680 \text{ MPa})(356 \text{ mm})}{12 \text{ mm}} = 49.8 \text{ MPa}$$

THE CORRECT ANSWER IS: B

32. Refer to the Uniaxial Loading and Deformation section in the Mechanics of Materials chapter of the *FE Reference Handbook.*

$P = 1{,}300$ lb $\quad A = (0.5)^2 \frac{\pi}{4} = 0.196 \text{ in}^2 \quad L = 12$ in.

$\delta = 0.009$ in.

$\delta = \frac{PL}{AE}$ rearranged gives

$$E = \frac{PL}{\delta A} = \frac{(1{,}300)(12)}{(0.009)(0.196)} = 8.84 \times 10^6 \text{ psi} = 8{,}840 \text{ ksi}$$

THE CORRECT ANSWER IS: C

Copyright © 2020 by NCEES

33. Refer to the Mohr's Circle section in the Mechanics of Material chapter of the *FE Reference Handbook.*

From a constructed Mohr's Circle, the maximum inplane shear stress is $\tau_{max} = R$.

$$R = \sqrt{\left(\frac{\sigma_x - \sigma_y}{2}\right)^2 + \tau_{xy}{}^2}$$

$$R = \sqrt{\left(\frac{40 - 20}{2}\right)^2 + 10^2}$$

$$R = \sqrt{200}$$

$$R = 14.1 \text{ ksi}$$

THE CORRECT ANSWER IS: B

34. Material B displays the most plastic deformation beyond a clear yield point.

THE CORRECT ANSWER IS: B

35. Refer to the Uniaxial Loading and Deformation section in the Mechanics of Materials chapter of the *FE Reference Handbook.*

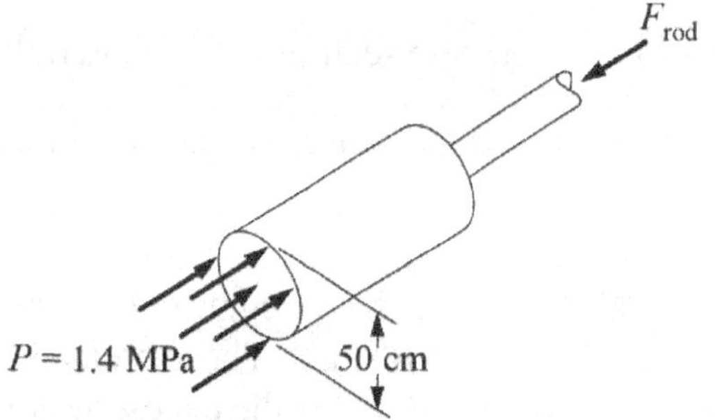

$$\Sigma F = PA = \left(1.4 \times 10^6\right)\left(\frac{\pi(0.5)^2}{4}\right) = F_{rod}$$

$$F_{rod} = 275 \text{ kN} = \sigma A = 68 \times 10^6 A$$

$$A = 40.4 \times 10^{-4} \text{ m}^2$$

THE CORRECT ANSWER IS: A

Copyright © 2020 by NCEES

36. Refer to the Torsion section in the Mechanics of Materials chapter of the *FE Reference Handbook.*

$$\tau = \frac{T\rho}{J}$$

$\therefore$ max τ when $\rho = r$

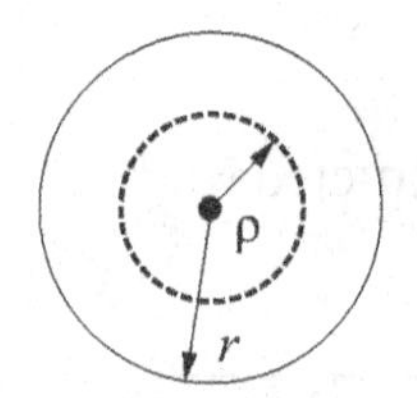

THE CORRECT ANSWER IS: A

37. Refer to the Concrete section in the Materials Science chapter of the *FE Reference Handbook.*

Because the concrete mix design specified a water-to-cement ratio, the most appropriate way to increase the slump of the concrete is to add an admixture that will increase the slump without affecting the water-to-cement ratio.

THE CORRECT ANSWER IS: C

38. Refer to the definition of *Charpy Impact Test* in the Materials Science/Structure of Matter chapter of the *FE Reference Handbook.*

THE CORRECT ANSWER IS: D

39. By definition, a metal with high hardness has a high tensile strength and a high yield strength.

THE CORRECT ANSWER IS: D

40. Refer to the Concrete section in the Materials Science chapter of the *FE Reference Handbook.*

The moisture content of each aggregate includes: (1) water that would be needed to bring aggregates to saturated surface dry (SSD) condition (the absorbed water) and (2) the excess water that is free to add to the mix water. Since the as-used moisture content is greater than the absorption for each aggregate, each aggregate contributes the excess water to the mix, thus reducing the water that must be added to mix. The water added to the mix is the water computed for oven-dry aggregates (305 lb/yd^3) plus the excess water in each aggregate.

Final water = 305 – [(2.0% – 0.5%)/100] × 1,674 – [(6.0% – 0.7%)/100] × 1,100 = 221.6 lb/yd^3

THE CORRECT ANSWER IS: B

Copyright © 2020 by NCEES

41. Refer to the Uniaxial Stress-Strain section in the Mechanics of Materials chapter of the *FE Reference Handbook.*

In accordance with the 0.2% offset method for identifying yield strength, a line parallel to the elastic portion of the stress-strain curve is passed through the strain axis at a value of 0.002. Where this line intersects the stress-strain curve is identified as the yield strength. Therefore, the slope of the dashed line is associated with the modulus of elasticity of the material.

THE CORRECT ANSWER IS: D

42. Refer to the Pitot Tube section in the Fluid Mechanics chapter of the *FE Reference Handbook.*

$$\frac{v^2}{2g} \approx \frac{(2)^2}{(2)(9.8)} \approx 0.204 \text{ m}$$

THE CORRECT ANSWER IS: D

43. Refer to the Stress, Pressure, and Viscosity section in the Fluid Mechanics chapter of the *FE Reference Handbook.*

Units of absolute dynamic viscosity (μ) are kg/(m·s).

Units of kinematic viscosity (v) are m^2/s.

∴ The relationship between the two is:

$v = \mu/\rho$ where ρ is the density in kg/m^3.

$v = 1.5/1.263(1{,}000) = 0.001188 = 1.19 \times 10^{-3}$.

THE CORRECT ANSWER IS: A

44. Refer to the Archimedes Principle and Buoyancy section in the Fluid Mechanics chapter of the *FE Reference Handbook.*

THE CORRECT ANSWER IS: D

Copyright © 2020 by NCEES

45. Refer to the Continuity Equation section in the Fluid Mechanics chapter of the *FE Reference Handbook.*

$$\rho = 1.94 \frac{\text{slug}}{\text{ft}^3} = 1.94 \text{ lb-sec}^2/\text{ft}^4$$

$$Q = A\text{v} = \frac{\pi}{4}\left(1 \text{ in.} \times \frac{\text{ft}}{12 \text{ in.}}\right)^2 \times 25\frac{\text{ft}}{\text{sec}} = 0.136\frac{\text{ft}^3}{\text{sec}}$$

$$F = \rho Q\left(\text{v}_2 - \text{v}_1\right)$$

Due to continuity: $\text{v}_2 = \text{v}_1 = 25$ ft/sec

$$F_x = \rho Q\left(\text{v}_{2x} - \text{v}_{1x}\right)$$

$$\text{v}_{2x} = \text{v}_2 \cos 45°$$

$$\text{v}_{1x} = \text{v}_1 \cos 45°$$

$$F_x = \rho Q\left(\text{v}_{2x} - \text{v}_{1x}\right) = \rho Q\left(\text{v}_2 \cos 45° - \text{v}_1 \cos 45°\right) = 0$$

$$F_y = \rho Q\left(\text{v}_{2y} - \text{v}_{1y}\right)$$

$$\text{v}_{2y} = \text{v}_2 \sin 45°$$

$$\text{v}_{1y} = -\text{v}_1 \sin 45°$$

$$F_y = 1.94 \text{ lb-sec}^2/\text{ft}^4 \times 0.136\frac{\text{ft}^3}{\text{sec}} \times \left[25\frac{\text{ft}}{\text{sec}} \times 0.707 - \left(-25\frac{\text{ft}}{\text{sec}} \times 0.707\right)\right] = 9.33 \text{ lb}$$

THE CORRECT ANSWER IS: C

Copyright © 2020 by NCEES

46. Refer to the Characteristics of a Static Liquid section in the Fluid Mechanics chapter of the *FE Reference Handbook.*

The mean pressure of the fluid acting on the gate is evaluated at the mean height, and the center of pressure is 2/3 of the height from the top; thus, the total force of the fluid is:

$$F_f = \rho g \frac{H}{2}(H) = 1{,}600(9.807)\frac{3}{2}(3) = 70{,}610 \text{ N}$$

and its point of application is 1.00 m above the hinge. A moment balance about the hinge gives:

$$F(3) - F_f(1) = 0$$

$$F = \frac{F_f}{3} = \frac{70{,}610}{3} = 23{,}537 \text{ N}$$

THE CORRECT ANSWER IS: C

47. Refer to the Orifice Discharging Freely into Atmosphere section in the Fluid Mechanics chapter of the *FE Reference Handbook.*

$$Q = CA_0(2gh)^{1/2}$$

$$Q = VA$$

$$V = C(2gh)^{1/2}$$

$$V_A = 0.6(2 \times 32.2 \text{ ft/sec}^2 \times 8 \text{ ft})^{1/2} = 13.6 \text{ ft/sec}$$

$$V_B = 0.6(2 \times 32.2 \text{ ft/sec}^2 \times 6 \text{ ft})^{1/2} = 11.8 \text{ ft/sec}$$

$$V_C = 0.6(2 \times 32.2 \text{ ft/sec}^2 \times 10 \text{ ft})^{1/2} = 15.2 \text{ ft/sec}$$

$$V_D = 0.6(2 \times 32.2 \text{ ft/sec}^2 \times 12 \text{ ft})^{1/2} = 16.7 \text{ ft/sec}$$

THE CORRECT ANSWER IS SHOWN.

Copyright © 2020 by NCEES

48. Refer to the Trigonometry section in the Mathematics chapter of the *FE Reference Handbook.*

Use Law of Cosines.

$a^2 = b^2 + c^2 - 2bc \cos A$

$$\cos A = \frac{480^2 + 720^2 - 390^2}{2(480)(720)}$$

A = 30° 18' 47"

THE CORRECT ANSWER IS: A

49. Refer to the Horizontal Curve Formulas section in the Civil Engineering chapter of the *FE Reference Handbook.*

Find the area of the fractional part of the circle.

$A = \pi r^2$

$A = \pi (500)^2$

$$\text{Fraction of circle} = \frac{36°48'}{360°} = \frac{36.8°}{360°} = 0.1022$$

$$\text{Area of fraction of circle} = 0.1022 \times \pi \times (500)^2 = 80{,}285 \text{ ft}^2$$

Shaded area = total area – fraction of circle

$= 83{,}164 - 80{,}285$

$= 2{,}879 \text{ ft}^2$

THE CORRECT ANSWER IS: A

50. Refer to the Earthwork Formulas section in the Civil Engineering chapter of the *FE Reference Handbook.*

Volume to be excavated = 130[322 + (4)(395) + 418]/[(6)(27)] = 1,862 yd^3

THE CORRECT ANSWER IS: C

Copyright © 2020 by NCEES

51. THE CORRECT ANSWER IS: D

52.

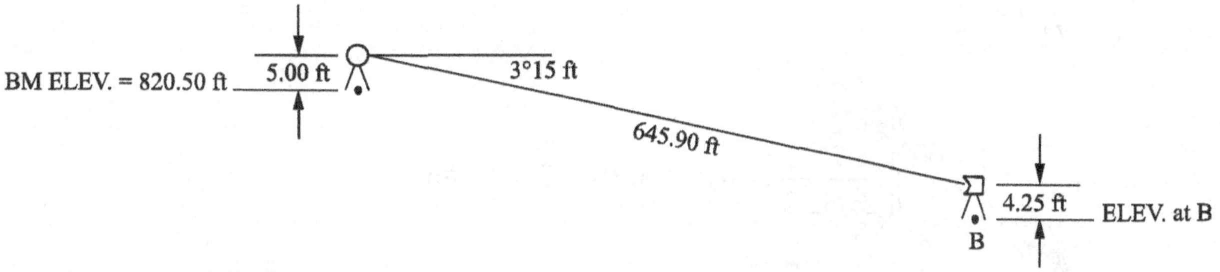

ELEV. at B = 820.50 + 5.00 – 645.90(sin 3.25) – 4.25 = 784.63

THE CORRECT ANSWER IS: B

53. TP elevation + backsight – foresight = pin elevation

2,325.58 + 7.76 – 4.25 = 2,329.09

THE CORRECT ANSWER IS: C

54. Refer to the Rational Formula section in the Civil Engineering chapter of the *FE Reference Handbook.*

$Q = CIA$

$Q = (0.10)(1.5 \text{ in./hr})(20 \text{ acres}) = 3.0 \text{ cfs}$

THE CORRECT ANSWER IS: A

Copyright © 2020 by NCEES

55. Refer to the Head Loss Due to Flow section in the Fluid Mechanics chapter of the *FE Reference Handbook.*

$$h_L = f\left(\frac{L}{D}\right)\left(\frac{v^2}{2g}\right)$$

$$h_{L,\text{AB}} = 0.03\left(\frac{200}{2}\right)\left(\frac{2^2}{2\times 32.2}\right) = 0.03(100)(0.062) = 0.186 \text{ ft}$$

$$h_{L,\text{AC}} = 0.03\left(\frac{200}{3}\right)\left(\frac{1.3^2}{2\times 32.2}\right) = 0.03(67)(0.026) = 0.052 \text{ ft}$$

$$h_{L,\text{CB}} = h_{L,\text{AB}} - h_{L,\text{AC}} = 0.186 - 0.052 = 0.134 \text{ ft}$$

Since the head loss from A to B is larger than the head loss from A to C, the head at C is greater than the head at B. This means there is flow from C to B.

THE CORRECT ANSWER IS: B

56. Refer to the Pressure Field in a Static Liquid section in the Fluid Mechanics chapter of the *FE Reference Handbook.*

Elevation difference:

$112 - 78 = 34$ ft

THE CORRECT ANSWER IS: B

Copyright © 2020 by NCEES

57. Refer to the Circular Pipe Head Loss Equation (ft) section in the Civil Engineering chapter of the *FE Reference Handbook.*

$$h_{f1} = \frac{4.73 L_1}{C^{1.852} D_1^{4.87}} Q^{1.852}$$

Parallel pipe flow: $h_{f1} = h_{f2}$

$(Q_1/Q_2)^{1.852} = (L_2/L_1) \times (D_1/D_2)^{4.87} = (1{,}200/2{,}400) \times (18/12)^{4.87} = 3.6$

$(Q_1/Q_2) = 3.6^{0.54} = 2$

$Q_1 + Q_2 = 3Q_2 = 15$ cfs

$Q_2 = 5$ cfs; $Q_1 = 10$ cfs

THE CORRECT ANSWER IS: B

58. Refer to the Weir Formulas section in the Civil Engineering chapter of the *FE Reference Handbook.*

Spillway head is 50 ft – 37 ft = 13 ft

$Q = CLH^{3/2}$ where $C = 3.33$ for rectangular weir (USCS unit)

$Q = 3.33(200 \text{ ft})(13^{3/2} \text{ ft}) = 31{,}216$, or 31,200 ft^3/sec

THE CORRECT ANSWER IS: D

Copyright © 2020 by NCEES

59. Refer to the Hydrology/Water Resources section in the Civil Engineering chapter of the *FE Reference Handbook.*

Solve for storage volume V_s (ac-ft)

$$V_s = V_r\left(\frac{V_s}{V_r}\right)$$

Drainage area: $A_m = 0.117$ mi^2

Frequency: 25 years

Runoff: Q = 3.4 in.

Runoff volume: $V_r = QA_m53.33$

where 53.33 = conversion factor from in-mi^2 to ac-ft

$V_r = 3.4$ in. $\times$ 0.117 mi^2 $\times$ 53.33 = 21.2 ac-ft

Peak inflow: $q_i = 360$ cfs

Peak outflow: $q_o = 180$ cfs

Compute: $q_o/q_i = 0.50$

Determine V_s/V_r from graph: 0.28

$$V_s = V_r\left(\frac{V_s}{V_r}\right)$$

$$V_s = 21.2(0.28) = 5.94 \text{ ac-ft}$$

THE CORRECT ANSWER IS: D

Copyright © 2020 by NCEES

60. Refer to the Manning's Equation section in the Civil Engineering chapter of the *FE Reference Handbook.*

Using Manning's equation: $V = \left(\frac{K}{n}\right) R_H^{2/3} S^{1/2}$

$$V = \left(\frac{1.486}{0.015}\right) 0.75^{2/3}\ 0.006^{1/2}$$

$V = 6.3$ ft/sec

Note: $K = 1.486$ for USCS units

R_H can be found from the Hydraulic-Elements Graph in the Civil Engineering chapter of the *FE Reference Handbook*

$d/D = 1.5/3 = 0.5$; therefore $R/R_{\text{full}} = 1.0$ (from graph)

$R_{\text{full}} = R = A/P = r/2 = 1.5/2 = 0.75$

THE CORRECT ANSWER IS: C

61. Velocity of flow is normal to lines of constant piezometric head. This is the line that connects points having the same head (A and C). The velocity vector is in the direction of decreasing head. In the figure, head decreases from B to D (the water table is higher at B, or the depth to the water table is less). Therefore, groundwater flows to the south.

THE CORRECT ANSWER IS: A

Copyright © 2020 by NCEES

62. Water Quality Category

Physical	Odor
	Turbidity
Chemical	Hardness
	Lead
Microbiological	*Giardia*
Radiological	Radon

Physical characteristics are often associated with the senses (e.g., taste, color, odor). Chemical characteristics often involve dissolved substances (minerals, metals, nutrients). Microbiological characteristics are associated with microorganisms and pathogens in particular (bacteria, viruses, protozoa). Radiological characteristics are associated with radioactive materials (artificial or natural).

THE CORRECT ANSWER IS SHOWN ABOVE.

63. Refer to the Design Criteria for Sedimentation Basins table in the Environmental Engineering chapter of the *FE Reference Handbook.*

Alum dosage is the one parameter the operator has control over during the coagulation process. Temperature, although it may have minor effect on coagulation efficiency, is typically outside the control of the operator. Dissolved oxygen plays no role in the efficacy of the coagulation process. Lime is used in hardness removal and thus not pertinent to coagulation.

THE CORRECT ANSWER IS: A

Copyright © 2020 by NCEES

64. Refer to the Structural Analysis section in the Civil Engineering chapter of the *FE Reference Handbook.*

The maximum force in CD occurs when the wheel is placed at the location that corresponds to the peak of the influence line:

Max F_{CD} = 1.875 × 20 kips = 37.5 kips

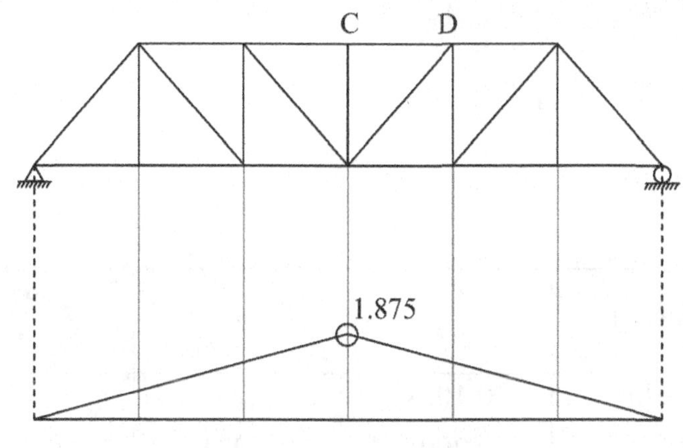

Influence line for CD

THE CORRECT ANSWER IS: C

Copyright © 2020 by NCEES

65. Refer to the Structural Analysis section in the Civil Engineering chapter of the *FE Reference Handbook.*

Apply a downward 1-kip load (unit load) at Joint C and compute forces f in bars. (This can easily be done by dividing each F force by 40).

Multiply each member's change in length $\Delta L = \frac{FL}{AE}$ by its force f in the table below (be sure to use the signed values of $\Delta L = \frac{FL}{AE}$ and f).

Then, sum $f \cdot \frac{FL}{AE}$ to get the displacement at Joint C.

$\sum f \cdot \frac{FL}{AE} = +\ 1.0464$ in. down

Member	F (kips)	L (in.)	$\frac{FL}{AE}$	f	$f \cdot \frac{FL}{AE}$
AB	50.0	240	0.1034	1.25	0.1292
BC	49.2	473	0.2008	1.231	0.2472
CD	–75.0	480	–0.3103	–1.875	0.5818
AD	–30.0	288	–0.0745	–0.75	0.0559
BD	–25.0	240	–0.0517	–0.625	0.0323
					$\sum = 1.0464$

THE CORRECT ANSWER IS: A

Copyright © 2020 by NCEES

66. Refer to the Columns section in the Mechanics of Materials chapter of the *FE Reference Handbook.*

A fundamental assumption of the Euler formulation for buckling is that the critical stress is less than the proportional limit (elastic buckling). The maximum length can be found by setting the critical stress equal to the proportional limit stress.

$$\sigma_{cr} = \frac{\pi^2 E}{\left(\frac{KL}{r}\right)^2} \le 40 \quad (1)$$

$$r = \sqrt{\frac{6.8}{9}} = 0.869 \quad (2)$$

Solving (1) for L

$L = 74.76 = 74.8$

THE CORRECT ANSWER IS: B

Copyright © 2020 by NCEES

67. Refer to the Stability, Determinacy, and Classification of Structures section in the Civil Engineering chapter of the *FE Reference Handbook.*

Unknown reactions and internal forces at internal pins: $6 \times 2 = 12$

Rigid body components (shown as FBDs) @ 3 equations per component: 4

Number of equations: $4 \times 3 = 12$

There are 12 equations and 12 unknowns → determinate (stable by member arrangement).

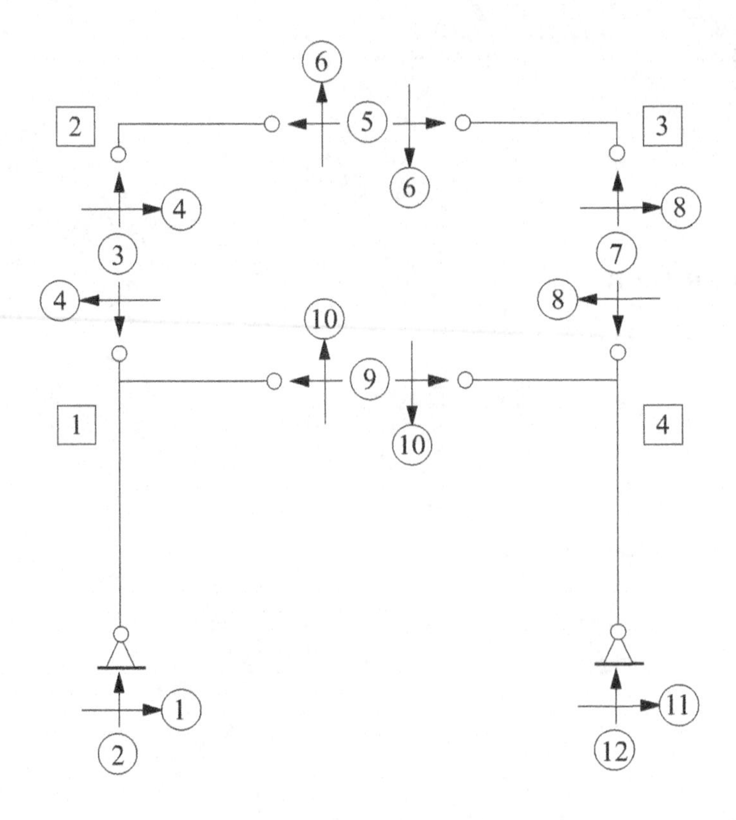

[1] RIGID BODY

(1) UNKNOWN FORCE

THE CORRECT ANSWER IS: B

68. Refer to the Beams section in the Mechanics of Materials chapter of the *FE Reference Handbook.*

The moment diagram and curvature of the deflected shape in Option B are consistent with the given convention.

THE CORRECT ANSWER IS: B

69. (A)

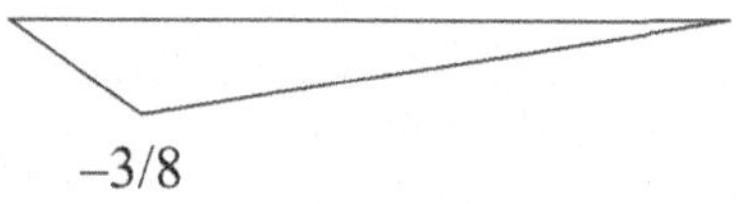

–3/8

(B)

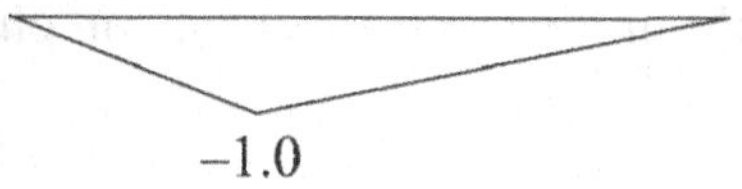

–1.0

(C)

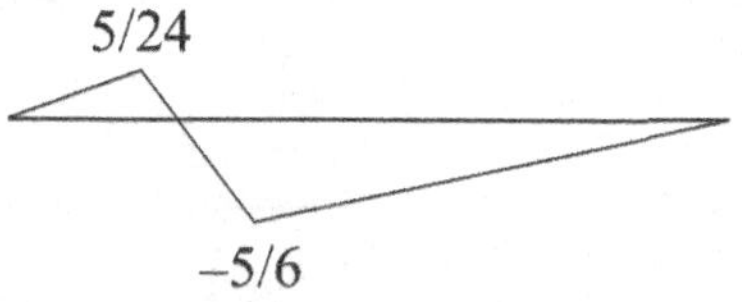

5/24

–5/6

(D)

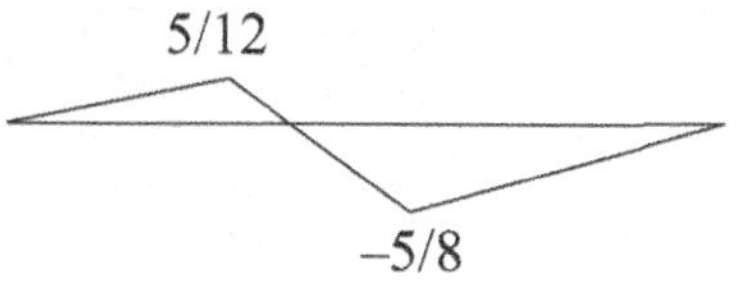

5/12

–5/8

THE CORRECT ANSWER IS: B

Copyright © 2020 by NCEES

70. **Method 1 (computation)** For bracing @ $L/3$: $L_b = 10.0$ ft and $C_b = 1.0$ (given)

From the Z_x table in the Civil Engineering chapter of the *FE Reference Handbook*, for W21 × 57: $\phi M_p = 484$ ft-kips $L_p = 4.77$ ft $L_r = 14.3$ ft BF = 20.1

Since $L_p < L_b$ (4.77 ft < 10 ft):

$\phi M_n = \phi M_p - \text{BF} \times (L_b - L_p) = 484 - 20.1 \times (10.0 - 4.77) = 378.9$ ft-kips

$$w_u = \frac{8\phi M_n}{L^2} = \frac{8 \times 378.9}{(30)^2} = 3.368 \text{ kips/ft}$$

Method 2 (graphical) For bracing @ $L/3$: $L_b = 10.0$ ft and $C_b = 1.0$ (given)

From the Available Moment vs. Unbraced Length table in the Civil Engineering chapter of the *FE Reference Handbook*:

Enter horizontal axis at $L_b = 10.0$ ft, and read upward to W21 × 57 curve: $\phi M_n = 378$

$$w_u = \frac{8\phi M_n}{L^2} = \frac{8 \times 378}{(30)^2} = 3.360 \text{ kips/ft}$$

THE CORRECT ANSWER IS: B

Copyright © 2020 by NCEES

71. Refer to the Design of Reinforced Concrete Components (ACI 318-11) section in the Civil Engineering chapter of the *FE Reference Handbook.*

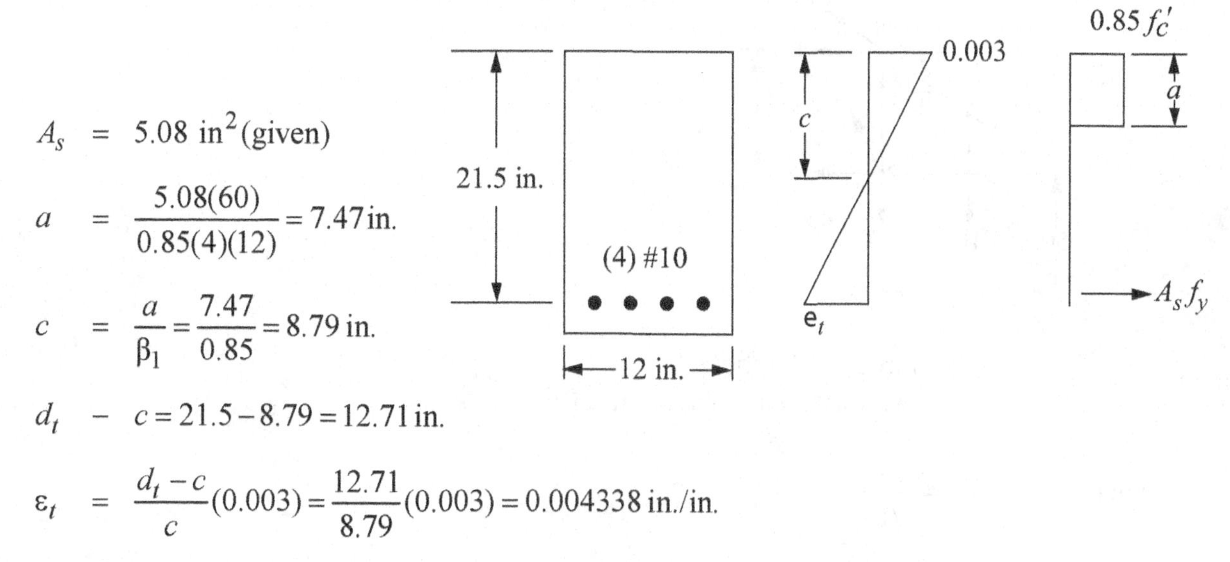

$$A_s = 5.08 \text{ in}^2 \text{(given)}$$

$$a = \frac{5.08(60)}{0.85(4)(12)} = 7.47 \text{ in.}$$

$$c = \frac{a}{\beta_1} = \frac{7.47}{0.85} = 8.79 \text{ in.}$$

$$d_t - c = 21.5 - 8.79 = 12.71 \text{ in.}$$

$$\varepsilon_t = \frac{d_t - c}{c}(0.003) = \frac{12.71}{8.79}(0.003) = 0.004338 \text{ in./in.}$$

Since $0.004 < \varepsilon_t < 0.005$, compute ϕ:

$$\phi = 0.48 + 83(0.004338) = 0.84004 = 0.84$$

THE CORRECT ANSWER IS: C

Copyright © 2020 by NCEES

72. Cut the truss through members CD, DK, and JK and draw a free-body diagram of the left side.

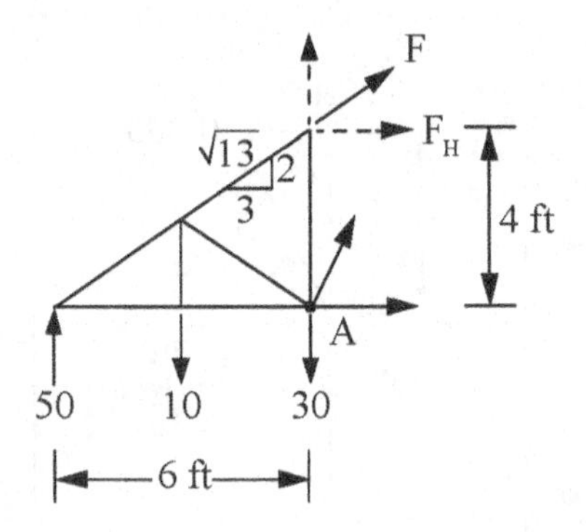

Let F = force in Member CD

F_H = the horizontal component of F

Then $F_H = \frac{3}{\sqrt{13}} F$

Solving for F: $F = \frac{\sqrt{13}}{3} F_H$

$\uparrow \sum M_A = 50 \text{ kips}(6 \text{ ft}) - 3 \text{ kips}(10 \text{ ft}) + F_H (4 \text{ ft}) = 0$

$F_H = -67.5 \text{ kips}(\text{comp})$

$F = \frac{\sqrt{13}}{3}(67.5 \text{ kips}) = 81.12 \text{ kips}(\text{comp})$

THE CORRECT ANSWER IS: A

Copyright © 2020 by NCEES

73. Refer to the Design of Reinforced Concrete Components (ACI 318-11) section in the Civil Engineering chapter of the *FE Reference Handbook.*

$$M_n = \frac{M_u}{\phi} = A_s f_y \left(d - \frac{a}{2}\right) = A_s f_y \left(d - \frac{1}{2} \times \frac{A_s f_y}{0.85\, f_c'\, b}\right)$$

where $A_s = 8 \times 0.79 \text{ in}^2 = 6.32 \text{ in}^2$

$d = 30 - 3.5 = 26.5$ in. (do not use $d_t = 27.5$ in.)

$$\frac{648 \times 12}{0.9} = 6.32 \times 60 \left(26.5 - \frac{1}{2} \times \frac{6.32 \times 60}{0.85 \times 4 \times b}\right)$$

$b = 14.98$ in. (use 15 in.)

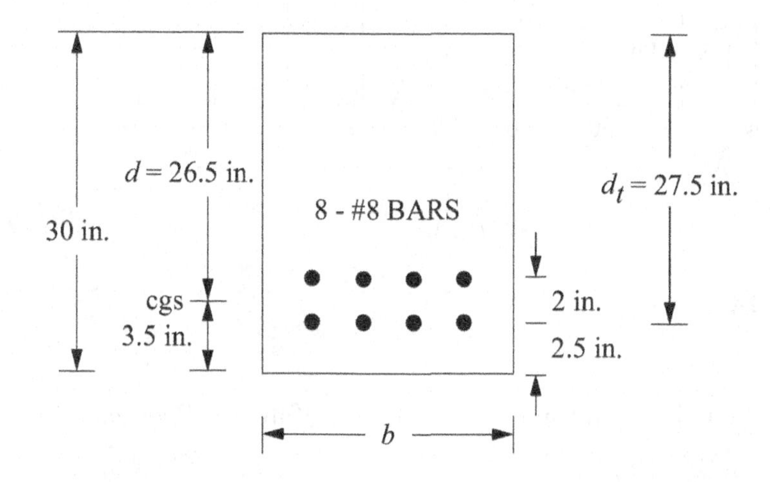

THE CORRECT ANSWER IS: D

Copyright © 2020 by NCEES

74. Refer to the Retaining Walls section in the Civil Engineering chapter of the *FE Reference Handbook.*

MH stands for an elastic silt. Anywhere below the "A" line and to the right of the LL = 50 line will satisfy this condition.

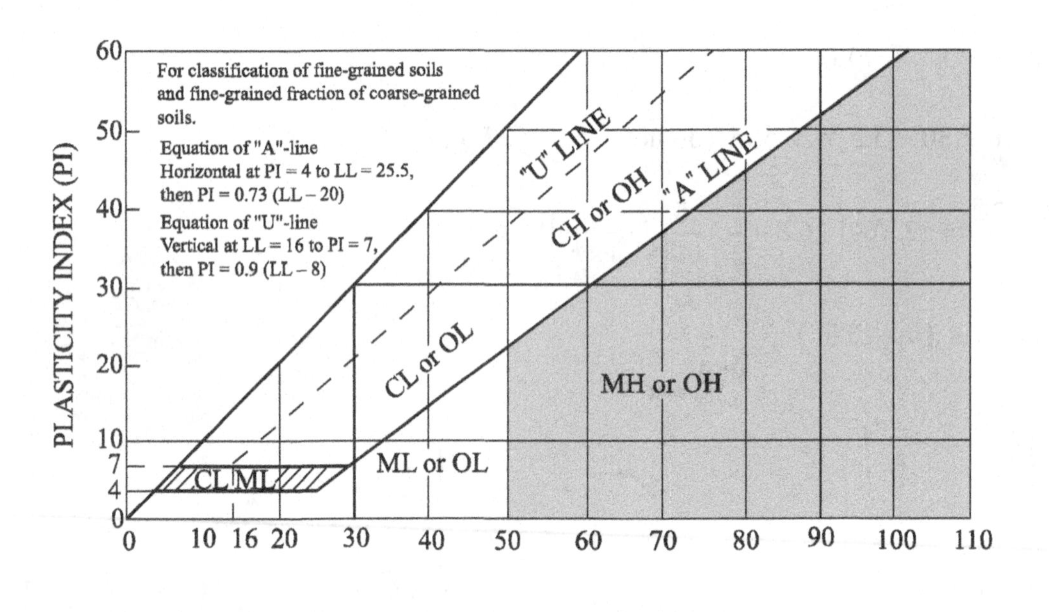

THE CORRECT ANSWER IS SHADED ABOVE.

75. Refer to the Geotechnical section in the Civil Engineering chapter of the *FE Reference Handbook.*

Degree of saturation = $S = \omega \, Gs/e$

$Gs \, \omega = Se$

$(2.7)(0.105) = S(0.63)$

$S = 45\%$

THE CORRECT ANSWER IS: B

Copyright © 2020 by NCEES

76. Refer to the Geotechnical section in the Civil Engineering chapter of the *FE Reference Handbook*.

$$\sigma_n = \frac{P}{A} = \frac{512 \text{ lb}}{16 \text{ in}^2} = 32 \text{ psi}$$

$\tau = 16$ psi

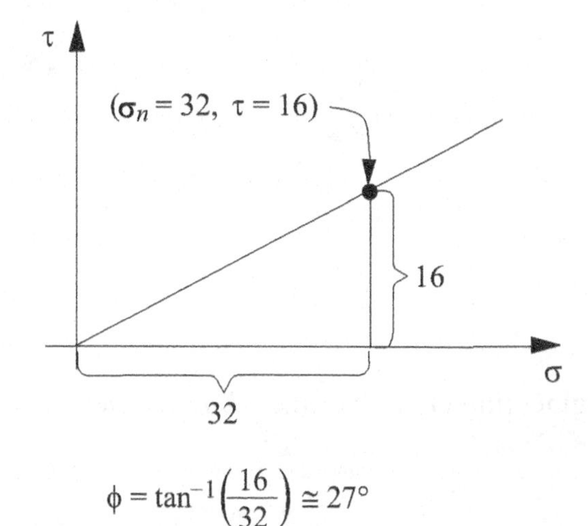

$$\phi = \tan^{-1}\left(\frac{16}{32}\right) \cong 27°$$

THE CORRECT ANSWER IS: B

77. Refer to Effective Stress in the Geotechnical section of the Civil Engineering chapter in the *FE Reference Handbook.*

$\sigma' = \sigma - u = (135 \times 10) - 62.4\,(10) = 726$ psf

THE CORRECT ANSWER IS: B

Copyright © 2020 by NCEES

78. Refer to the Geotechnical section in the Civil Engineering chapter of the *FE Reference Handbook.*

$H = 12$ ft
$\phi = 30°$
$\gamma = 125$ pcf

$K_A = \tan^2(45° - \phi/2)$
$= \tan^2(45° - 30/2)$
$= 0.3333$

$P_A = 1/2\ \gamma\ H^2 K_A$
$= 1/2\ (125\text{ pcf})\ (12\text{ ft})^2\ (0.333)$
$= 2{,}998$ plf

THE CORRECT ANSWER IS: B

79. Refer to the Geotechnical section in the Civil Engineering chapter of the *FE Reference Handbook.*

$d = 1.4$ in., so $A = \pi r^2 = 1.54\text{ in}^2$
$c = 530\text{ psf} = 3.68\text{ psi}$

$\phi = 18°$

$P = 125$ lb

$$\sigma_N = \frac{P}{A}$$

$\tau_F = c + \sigma_N \tan\phi$
$\sigma_N = 125\text{ lb}/1.54\text{ in}^2 = 81.2\text{ psi}$
$\tau_F = 3.68\text{ psi} + (81.2\text{ psi})\tan 18 = 30\text{ psi}$

THE CORRECT ANSWER IS: C

Copyright © 2020 by NCEES

80. Refer to the Ultimate Bearing Capacity section in the Civil Engineering chapter of the *FE Reference Handbook.*

$q_{ult} = cN_c + \gamma D_f N_q + 0.5\ \gamma B N_\gamma$

Since $N_c = 0$ and $D_f = 0$,

$$q_{ult} = (0.5)(120)(2)(25) = 3{,}000 \text{ psf}$$

THE CORRECT ANSWER IS: C

81. The upper soils are so weak that spread footings would be too large. A good rule of thumb for buildings is that spread footings cease to be economical when the total plan area of the footings exceeds about one-third of the building footprint area.

THE CORRECT ANSWER IS: C

82. Refer to the Geotechnical section in the Civil Engineering chapter of the *FE Reference Handbook.*

$t = T\,H_{dr}^2/c_v = 1.2\ (5 \times 5)/0.16 = 187.5$ days

THE CORRECT ANSWER IS: C

Copyright © 2020 by NCEES

83. Refer to the Retaining Walls section in the Civil Engineering chapter of the *FE Reference Handbook.*

Given:
L_s = 100 ft
α_s = 27°
W_M = 100 tons = 200,000 lb
ϕ = 20°
c = 1.2 psi = 173 psf

$$FS = \frac{T_{FF}}{T_{MOB}} = \frac{cL_s + W_M \cos\alpha_s \tan\phi}{W_M \sin\alpha_s}$$

FS = (173 psf)(100 ft) + (200,000 lb)(cos 27°)(tan 20°)/(200,000 lb)(sin 27°) = 0.9

THE CORRECT ANSWER IS: B

84. Refer to the Transportation section in the Civil Engineering chapter of the *FE Reference Handbook.*

Try equation for $S \leq L$

$$L = \frac{AS^2}{100\left[\sqrt{2h_1} + \sqrt{2h_2}\right]^2}$$

$$= \frac{9 \times 600^2}{100\left[\sqrt{2 \times 3.50} + \sqrt{2 \times 1.00}\right]^2}$$

$$= 1{,}966 \text{ ft}$$

$S \leq L$ as assumed. Therefore, the correct equation was used.

THE CORRECT ANSWER IS: B

Copyright © 2020 by NCEES

85. Refer to the Highway Pavement Design section in the Civil Engineering chapter of the *FE Reference Handbook.*

$$2.50 = 0.44(2) + 0.25(4) + 0.10(D_3)$$

$$D_3 = \frac{2.50 - 0.88 - 1.00}{0.10} = \frac{0.62}{0.10} = 6.2 \text{ in.}$$

THE CORRECT ANSWER IS: C

86. Refer to the Transportation section in the Civil Engineering chapter of the *FE Reference Handbook.*

$$\text{Spacing} = \frac{3{,}600 \text{ sec/hr}}{1{,}400 \text{ vehicles/hr}} = 2.57 \text{ sec/vehicle}$$

THE CORRECT ANSWER IS: A

87. WALK + width/pedestrian speed = green

$6 + 31.5/3.5 = 15.0$

THE CORRECT ANSWER IS: D

Copyright © 2020 by NCEES

88. Refer to the Traffic Safety Equations section in the Civil Engineering chapter of the *FE Reference Handbook.*

Crash factors are not additive, so combined CR

$CR = CR_1 + (1 - CR_1)\, CR_2$ (order CRs from highest to lowest)

$= 0.25 + (1 - 0.25)0.15$

$= 0.36$

1 since no change in ADT

$$\text{Crashes prevented} = N \times CR \left(\frac{\text{ADT after}}{\text{ADT before}}\right)$$

$3.6 = 10 \times 0.36$

$10 - 3.6 = 6.4$

THE CORRECT ANSWER IS: D

89. Departure sight triangles are based on a vehicle stopped at the stop bar and looking at major street vehicles for acceptable gaps.

THE CORRECT ANSWER IS: B

90. Asphalt or any combination with asphalt will be thicker under identical conditions.

THE CORRECT ANSWER IS: C

Copyright © 2020 by NCEES

91. Refer to the Basic Freeway Segment Highway Capacity section in the Civil Engineering chapter of the *FE Reference Handbook.*

Option A: Not true. A 75-mph free-flow speed freeway has a breakpoint of 1,000 pc/h/ln, while a 55-mph freeway has a breakpoint of 1,800 pc/h/ln. The breakpoint is defined by the *Highway Capacity Manual* as the volume for which the operating speeds becomes lower than the free-flow speed.

Option B: True. The free-flow speed is impacted by the lane width, right side lateral clearance, and the total ramp density (TRD).

Option C: True. The capacity of a 75-mph free-flow speed freeway is 2,400 pc/h/ln, while a similar facility with a 55-mph free-flow speed has a capacity of 2,250 pc/h/ln.

Option D: Not true. Lane widths equal to 12 ft and greater have the same free-flow speed. Increasing lane widths only increases speeds when the lane widths are 12 ft or less.

Option E: Not true. The estimated operating speed is impacted only once the volumes exceed the breakpoint volume; therefore there is no impact to operating speed changes in volumes when traffic volumes are low.

THE CORRECT ANSWERS ARE: B, C

92. Refer to the Logit Models section in the Civil Engineering chapter of the *FE Reference Handbook.*

$$P(x) = \frac{e^{Ux}}{\sum_{x=1}^{n} e^{Uxi}}$$

Three modes available: drive alone, carpool, and transit

$$P(x) = \frac{e^{U\text{carpool}}}{e^{U\text{carpool}} + e^{U\text{drive alone}} + e^{U\text{transit}}}$$

$$P(x) = \frac{e^{-0.40}}{e^{-0.40} + e^{1.2} + e^{-0.65}} = \frac{0.67}{0.67 + 3.32 + 0.52} = 0.15 = 15\%$$

THE CORRECT ANSWER IS: B

Copyright © 2020 by NCEES

93. **THE CORRECT ANSWER IS: C**

94. Refer to the Materials Handling section in the Industrial and Systems chapter of the *FE Reference Handbook.*

Time to load one truck = 15 yd^3/3 yd^3/min
= 5 min

Four trucks are available.
Cycle time for one truck = 5 min loading plus 12 min to travel, dump, and return = 17 min.
Loading time for four trucks = 4 × 5 = 20 min.

Therefore, an empty truck is always available to load.

$$\text{Ideal production capacity} = \left(\frac{60\,\text{min/ hr}}{5\,\text{min/ truck}}\right)\left(15\frac{\text{yd}^3}{\text{truck}}\right)$$
$$= 180\frac{\text{yd}^3}{\text{hr}}$$

THE CORRECT ANSWER IS: A

95. Refer to the Indices section in the Civil Engineering chapter of the *FE Reference Handbook.*

A cost performance index (CPI) greater than 1.0 indicates a cost savings, and a schedule performance index (SPI) of less than 1.0 indicates the project is behind schedule.

THE CORRECT ANSWER IS: A

96. Dry unit weight of embankment material $= 122\left(\frac{100}{(100+16.7)}\right)$
$= 104.5$ pcf

Volume required $= \frac{104.5}{106}(320{,}000)$
$= 315{,}470 \text{ yd}^3$

THE CORRECT ANSWER IS: B

Copyright © 2020 by NCEES

97. Orthographic views represent the top, front, and side views, and are arranged as shown below:

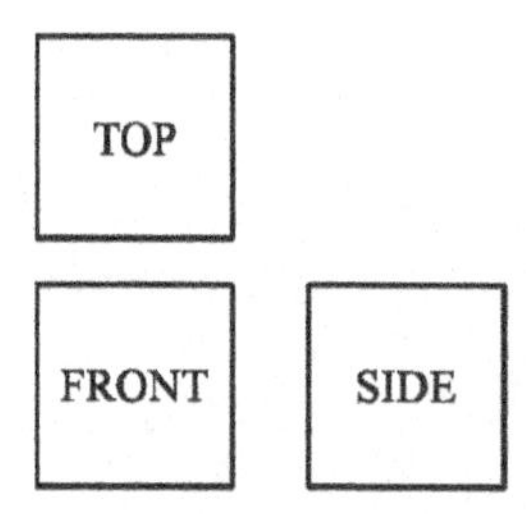

Option A: The top view is reversed horizontally, and the side and top views do not match.

Option C: The top view is rotated and reversed, and neither the front or side views match the top view.

Option D: The top view is reversed vertically, and the side and top views do not match.

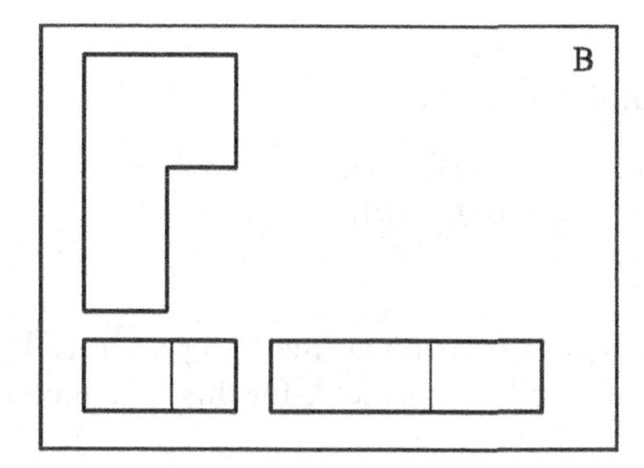

THE CORRECT ANSWER IS: B

98. Refer to the Materials Handling section in the Industrial and Systems chapter of the *FE Reference Handbook.*

$$\text{Production of Excavator 3} = \frac{60 \text{ min/hr}}{0.50 \text{ min cycle}} \times 1.75 \text{ LCY capacity} = 210 \text{ LCY/hr}$$

Similar calculations for the other three excavators show they have lower production rates.

THE CORRECT ANSWER IS: C

Copyright © 2020 by NCEES

99. Refer to the Earned-Value Analysis section in the Civil Engineering chapter of the *FE Reference Handbook.*

BCWP / ACWP = CPI
$3,200 / $3,400 = 0.9412

(BAC – BCWP) / CPI = ETC
($4,000 – $3,200) / 0.9412 = $850

Estimate at completion:
ACWP + ETC = EAC
$3,400 + $850 = $4,250

THE CORRECT ANSWER IS: C

100. The arrow and number indicate the cross slope of the roadway.

$$\frac{3\text{ in}}{12\text{ in./ft}} = \frac{0.25}{10\text{ ft}} = 0.025\text{ ft/ft}\ \ 3\text{-in./12 in./ft} = 0.25/10\text{ ft} = 0.025\text{ ft/ft.}$$

Slopes of road or bridge cross-sections are expressed as ft/ft and normally represented by a number, in this case 0.025. Slopes can also be expressed as a percent; for this case it could be expressed as 2.5%.

THE CORRECT ANSWER IS: B

Copyright © 2020 by NCEES

FE EXAM PREPARATION MATERIAL
PUBLISHED BY NCEES

FE Reference Handbook

FE Practice Exams for all modules:
Chemical
Civil
Electrical and Computer
Environmental
Industrial and Systems
Mechanical
Other Disciplines

For more information about these and other NCEES publications and services, visit us at www.ncees.org or contact Client Services at (800) 250-3196.

Copyright ©2020 by NCEES